Curri**CUL**m Focus

Animals, plants and habitats

Catherine & Anthony Yemm

HOPSCOTCH
A division of MA Education Ltd

Curriculum Focus series

History

Toys Key Stage 1
Famous Events Key Stage 1
Famous People Key Stage 1
Invaders Key Stage 2
Tudors Key Stage 2

Geography

Islands and Seasides Key Stage 1
The Local Area Key Stage 1

Science

Ourselves Key Stage 1
Plants and Animals Key Stage 1
Materials Key Stage 1

Published by Hopscotch
A division of MA Education Ltd
St Jude's Church, Dulwich Road
Herne Hill, London SE24 0PB
Tel: 020 7738 5454
© 2008 MA Education Ltd

Written by Catherine Yemm
Linked ICT activities by Michelle Singleton
Series design by Blade Communications
Illustrated by David Burroughs
Cover illustration by Felicity House
Printed in the UK by CLE

Catherine Yemm hereby asserts her moral right to be
identified as the author of this work in accordance with
the Copyright, Designs and Patents Act, 1988.

ISBN 9-781-90430-757-0

Contents

Cross-curricular links 4

Introduction 5

1 Plants around us 6

2 Growing plants 15

3 Plants as food 23

4 Water and plants 31

5 Plants and light 41

6 Plants and animals around us 50

7 Habitats 60

8 Seeds of flowering plants 70

9 Growing seeds 79

10 Life cycles 87

11 Recognising characteristics 98

12 Similarities: humans and animals 108

13 Similarities and differences: plants 117

14 Measuring differences 127

15 Grouping living things 134

Photocopiable word banks 145

Cross-curricular links

Chapter	Science SoW	Art SoW	Literacy framework	Numeracy framework	ICT SoW
1	Unit 1B		Y1, Term 1: T12, T14 Y1, Term 2: T22 Y1, Term 3: T19		Unit 1B
2	Unit 1B		Y1, Term 1: T12, T14 Y1, Term 2: T22		Unit 2B
3	Unit 1B		Y1, Term 1: T12, T14	Y1: Handling data	Unit 1E
4	Unit 1B		Y1, Term 1: T12, T14 Y1, Term 2: T22 Y1, Term 1: S4		Unit 2A
5	Unit 1B	Unit 2B	Y1, Term 1: S4		Unit 2B
6	Unit 2B		Y1, Term 1: T12, T14 Y1, Term 2: T22		Units 1B/2A
7	Unit 2B		Y1, Term 1: T12, T14 Y1, Term 2: T22 Y1, Term 3: T19		Unit 1C
8	Unit 2B		Y1, Term 1: T12, T14 Y1, Term 2: T22		Unit 2B
9	Unit 2B		Y1, Term 1: S4		Units 1B/2A
10	Unit 2B	Unit 2B	Y1, Term 1: T12, T14 Y1, Term 2: T22		Unit 2B
11	Unit 2B		Y1, Term 1: T12, T14 Y1, Term 2: T22 Y1, Term 1: S4		Units 1D/2E
12	Unit 2C		Y1, Term 1: S4 KS1 NC Speaking and listening		Unit 1C
13	Unit 2C		KS1 NC Speaking and listening Y1, Term 1: T12, T14 Y1, Term 2: T22		Unit 1B
14	Unit 2C		KS1 NC Speaking and listening	Y1: Handling data	Unit 2E
15	Unit 2C		Y1, Term 1: T12, T14 Y1, Term 2: T22	Y1: Handling data	Unit 1D

Introduction

Curriculum Focus: Animals, Plants and Habitats Key Stage 1 helps to make science fun by giving you (especially those of you who are not science specialists) the support you need to plan stimulating and exciting lessons.

This book will help you to plan and teach a unit of work based on the QCA Scheme of Work for Science at Key Stage 1. Also, where appropriate, this book gives indications as to how the work can be linked with other areas of the curriculum.

The material in this book gives you a sound foundation from which to plan a unit of work for your classes.

The material includes:

- detailed **Teachers' notes** giving **background information** on each topic and/or concept to be taught;
- fully illustrated **Generic sheets** offering a wealth of resource material that can be used again and again;
- a **Lesson plan** full of ideas for introducing and developing the lesson;
- photocopiable and **differentiated Activity sheets** to support individual and group work.

Any unit of work on science must involve an opportunity to carry out practical activities. The work will be enhanced by visits to local environments where the children will learn from studying the plants and animals in their natural habitats.

Each chapter in the book is related to a specific unit from the QCA Scheme of Work for Science at Key Stage 1.

Chapters 1 to 5 relate to Unit 1B.
Chapters 6 to 11 relate to Unit 2B.
Chapters 12 to 15 relate to Unit 2C.

Curriculum Focus: Animals, Plants and Habitats Key Stage 1 recognises that there will be different levels of attainment among the children and that their developing literacy skills will require different levels of support during individual and group work. To help you provide activities that meet the needs of your classes, each chapter contains three photocopiable sheets based on the same material, but for children of different levels of attainment. This enables the whole class to take part in a similar activity.

- Activity sheet 1 in each chapter is intended for lower-attaining children.
- Activity sheet 2 is suitable for most children.
- Activity sheet 3 challenges the higher-attaining children.

CHAPTER 1

Plants around us

A plant is a living organism, usually characterised by having leaves, a stem and roots. Green plants are the only living things that can manufacture their own food through the highly specialised process of photosynthesis. Most plants (but not all) have a vascular system, which is involved in the movement of water and minerals. Plants respire, require nutrition, reproduce, move, grow, excrete and are sensitive to their environment. Most plants are terrestrial although some live in water.

Different plants in the environment

Different environments will support different plants. Many factors affect which plants live in which environment. The climate of an area – the temperature, humidity, wind strength and rainfall – affects plants. Plants such as the cactus or palm tree favour warmer temperatures, while the Scots pine tree grows quite happily in much colder temperatures. Most plants will flourish as long as enough water is available for them to survive, and a plentiful supply of rain may even increase their growth and reproduction. But if a plant receives too much water, then lack of oxygen to the roots can cause it to drown, or persistent wetness may cause the roots to rot. Some plants are structured so that they will be able to resist strong winds – such plants may be found in coastal areas. Others may have a more delicate structure and will prefer more sheltered environments where wind is at a minimum. Some plants can tolerate a great climatic range, while for others even the smallest deviation from the favoured climate could result in unhealthy growth.

Soil is another factor that influences the types of plants that grow in a certain environment. Soil types can be acidic, alkaline, sandy or heavy with clay. The roots of a plant penetrate the soil to gain water and nutrients, and a plant will grow best in a soil that provides the specific elements that it needs. Too many unwanted factors, such as high levels of lime, could be damaging to some plants, while others would flourish in a soil of this kind.

Other factors affecting the type of plant that lives in a certain area may be the amount of sunlight and shade present. Plants such as poppies need a regular supply of sunlight to grow properly, while shade-loving plants such as bluebells would probably not flourish if exposed to continuous direct sunlight.

The presence of other plant inhabitants will also have an effect on which plants grow and survive in a particular area. When more than one species of plant is living in the same environment, then interaction between them is often inevitable. If the interaction between the species is beneficial for both, and both grow healthily without any problems, this is known as 'mutualism' or 'symbiosis'. Often one species benefits at another species' expense – for example, mistletoe grows parasitically on oak trees, robbing them of water and nutrients. The term for this kind of interaction is 'competition'. Other organisms such as animals, fungi and bacteria also live in the same specific environment as a plant, and they may interact with the plants in a mutualistic or competitive way.

Different places they grow

When looking in an immediate environment, children usually think that plants only grow in the soil they can see on the ground. But a closer look will reveal that plants are living and reproducing in a multitude of places. Algae, mosses and liverworts are all plants. Algae grow on a variety of surfaces such as water, rocks, soil and tree trunks. Mosses and liverworts favour damp places and can grow anywhere, including on walls and roofs. Some plants live on or in other plants – for example, bramble plants, which often live in hedgerows.

Structure of plants

The structure of green plants is designed to allow them to catch the light of the Sun, which they then use to synthesise their own food. The roots of a plant anchor it to the ground and bear root hairs by which the plant takes in water and nutrients. The stem contains tubes and the water and nutrients taken up by the roots are transported around the plant through these tubes. The stem also supports the leaves and flowers of the plant. The leaves of most green plants are usually green but may change colour depending on the season. The green colour is due to the green pigment, called 'chlorophyll', present in the cells of the leaf. These special cells, called 'chloroplasts', allow the process of photosynthesis to take place, where energy (from sunlight), water and carbon dioxide are converted into glucose (food) for the plant and oxygen. Leaf surfaces are also dotted with tiny holes called 'stomata'. Air and water can move through these holes. Some plants also have flowers, which are used for reproduction.

Plants you may find in your local environment

The plant kingdom includes algae, mosses, ferns, conifers and flowering plants (broad-leafed trees are flowering plants). Here are some examples of plants that can be found in different local environments, but there are obviously many more.

Environment	Plants
Town	Ivy, shepherd's-purse, moss, lichen
Country	Oak, poppy, primrose, bluebell
Coast	Common scurvy grass, marram grass, sea kale, golden samphire

Walking around the local area

When organising a walk to look at the plants that grow in your local environment, it is important to comply with the local education authority's guidelines for taking children on a visit. The adult-to-child ratio must be strictly adhered to, even if you are only taking the children a short distance away from the school.

It will help if you visit the area yourself beforehand, so that you can assess any potential dangers or obstacles and complete a risk assessment. Visiting the area will also give you the chance to observe things to show the children and to assess whether the area will provide them with enough examples of plants to look at.

- Consult the school and local authority guidelines that deal with taking children out of school. These will cover all the key points of administrative detail and ensure that you have completed all the necessary risk assessments.

- Check that you have enough adult helpers – again, guidelines will detail how many are essential. Aim for at least one adult for every ten children, although more is better.

- Walk the route yourself first, and highlight potential danger points, such as road crossing points, and what you intend to do about them.

- Brief all your adult helpers as to what you want the children to do. Ensure they understand why they are going out, what you expect of them and exactly what you want each child to do and to have achieved/experienced by the end of the visit.

- Make sure that you gain parental approval if this is deemed necessary by the headteacher, school and local education authority.

- Take adequate first-aid equipment with you and make sure that you have enough adults who know how to use it.

- Make sure that the children understand exactly why they are going out and what you want them to do, as well as how you expect them to behave.

- Ensure that you are clear about what you will do if the weather is poor on the day or becomes poor during the outing.

- Don't aim to be out for longer than about 45 minutes.

Treating plants with care

When out looking for plants that grow in their local environment, the children must remember the importance of not picking or touching the plants that they see. Some plants are poisonous or can cause an allergic reaction. Delicate leaves and petals may be damaged by touch. If picked, plants will eventually die – in only a few hours their appearance will change and they will wither and become limp due to lack of water in their cells. Remind the children that the plant may be a home for animals and that they will not learn anything more about the plant by holding it, so they should leave it growing where it is.

Plants around us

> ### Science objectives (Unit 1B)
> - To know that there are different plants in the immediate environment.
> - To treat growing plants with care.
> - To make careful observations of one or two plants and of where they grow and to communicate these.
> - To know that plants have leaves, stems and flowers.

Resources

- Generic sheets 1 and 2 (pages 10 and 11)
- Activity sheets 1–3 (pages 12–14)
- Potted plant
- Coloured stickers
- Large, simplified map of the area
- OHP
- Clipboards
- Plain A4 paper
- Plant reference book

Starting points: *whole class*

Explain to the children that they are going to learn about plants and how they grow. Ask them if they can explain what a plant is. Ask one of the children to describe what a plant might look like. Show the children a potted plant that you have brought into the classroom. Using Generic sheet 1, ask them to help you label the leaves, stem, roots and flower of the plant. Explain the roles of the various parts of the plant as you label them. (The leaves help the plant produce its own food. The stem moves water and nutrients around the plant, and supports the leaves and flowers. The roots absorb water and anchor the plant. The flowers help the plant reproduce itself.)

Ask the children where they think they could find a plant to look at. Discuss indoor plants that may be in pots, which people look after, and plants that live outdoors naturally and look after themselves. Children may not realise that a tree or moss is a plant. Cut out the cards on Generic sheet 2 and show them to the children one at a time. Ask them to help you sort the pictures into two groups, writing them on the board under the headings 'a plant' and 'not a plant'. Each time you show them a new card, ask them if they think it is a plant and what sort of plant it is.

Fieldwork

Take the children for a walk in your local environment and ask them to look for plants that are growing there. Before you set out, remind them of the importance of not touching the plants or picking them.

Take with you a large simplified map of the area you are visiting. Show the children some coloured stickers and explain that each different colour will stand for a type of plant – for example, moss has a red sticker, trees have a yellow one, grass blue and flowers brown. You could decide on a key for the coloured stickers before you go for your walk and take it with you as a reference. Ask the children to look around and see if they can recognise types of plants growing in the area. Ask them to feed back information about the plants they can see and put stickers on the map to show where plants of a certain type were found.

Give the children a clipboard and some plain paper and encourage them to draw pictures of plants they see. Encourage them to look closely at the plant and ask them questions such as 'What shape are the leaves?' and 'Does the plant have a flower?' It may be useful to take a plant reference book with you on your walk, so that you can look up the names of some of the plants that you see.

Group activities

Tell the children that they are going to label some pictures of plants.

Activity sheet 1

This sheet is aimed at children who need more support. Using this sheet the children have to match pictures to the names of types of plants they might find in their local environment. They also have to label the main parts of a plant that they are likely to have seen before and colour the parts of the plant.

Activity sheet 2

This sheet is aimed at children who can work independently. Using this sheet the children have to label different types of plants with the help of a word bank. On the back of the sheet, they have to draw a plant they have seen in their local environment, label its main parts and write a caption saying what sort of plant it is.

Activity sheet 3

This sheet is aimed at more able children. They have to draw pictures to match types of plants, and label given pictures. On the back of the sheet, they have to draw two plants that they saw in their local environment, write captions and label their main parts.

Plenary session

Look at the site map where you placed the stickers. Ask the children if they can see any patterns. Are all the trees in one place? Are all the flowering plants in an open spot? Ask them to show their drawings, say where they found them and talk about the parts of the plants.

Ideas for support

Some children will need help with reading the words on the activity sheet. Display a word bank in the classroom with words such as 'stem', 'leaf', 'root' and 'flower'.

While on the walk in the local environment, take photographs of some of the plants the children find. The plants could then be named and the photographs could be displayed in the classroom as examples of the plants that can be found in the local environment.

Show the children how to add captions and labels to their drawings and photographs.

Ideas for extension

Ask the children to find out the names of three plants that grow best in the shade and three plants that grow best in the sunlight.

Ask them to look for two plants in their own or someone else's garden. They should draw the plants and write captions about what sort of plants they are; for example, moss or tree. They should then write a sentence about what sort of area they were found in; for example, under a shady tree or on a damp wall.

Ask the children to design a poster to warn other people not to pick or touch plants.

Linked ICT activities

Using 'Talking Write Away', 'Teaxtease', 'Clicker 4' or any other similar program that allows you to create word banks, create a word bank that contains words the children will recognise as parts of a plant. Mix these words with other words that may be parts of the human body, for example. The children will need to read the words in the word bank before using them.

Show them how to change the font style, size and colour of words in the word bank.

Then ask the children to choose five words from the word bank that are the names of the parts of a plant. Having chosen the words, they should change the font style, size and colour to make labels for the wall display. Print out the words, cut them out and add them to the wall display.

Plants around us

Label the plant.

Plants around us

moss	lichen	grass	conifer
stone	dog	flowering plant	tree
hedgerow	fern	pondweed	child

Name _____

Plants around us

Match the words and the pictures.

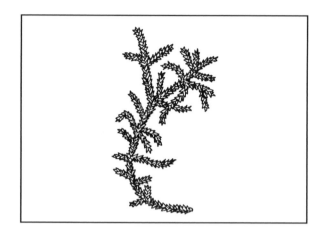 

| grass | moss | flowering plant | tree |

Now colour the plant below using the correct colours. Match the labels to the parts of the plant.

flower

leaves

stem

Name _____

Plants around us

Choose the correct words from the word bank to match the pictures.

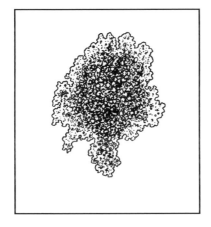

Word bank

flowering plant　　　tree　　　lichen　　　grass　　　fern

On the back of this sheet, draw a plant you saw in your local environment. Write a caption to say what sort of plant it is. Label the main parts of the plant.

Plants around us

Fill in the missing words and draw the missing pictures.

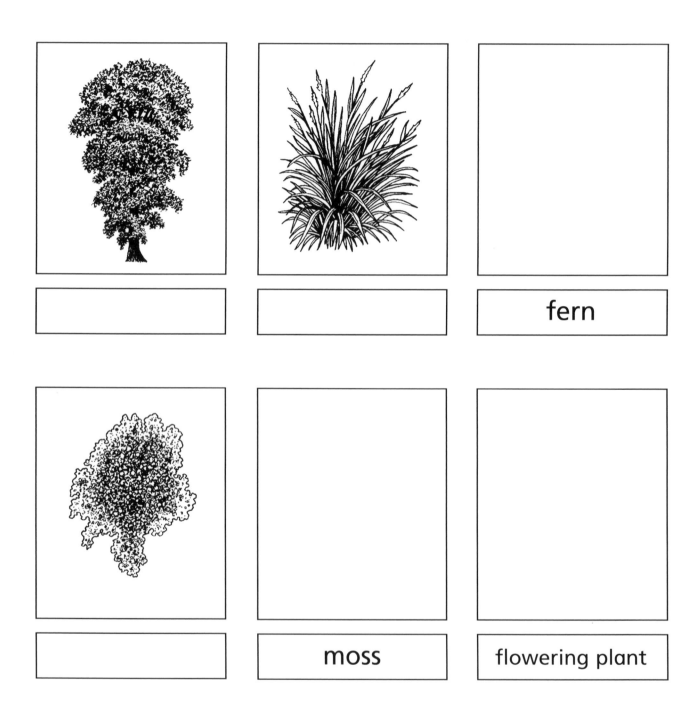

| | | fern |
| | | |

| | moss | flowering plant |

On the back of this sheet, draw two different types of plant you saw in your local environment. Write captions to say what sort of plants they are. Label the main parts of the plants.

Growing plants

TEACHERS' NOTES

Plant uses

Plants are grown for a number of reasons – the primary reason being as a source of food. Nearly all of our food supply is provided by flowering plants and is mostly eaten in the form of fruit, grains and vegetables or, indirectly, by plants being fed to animals. Plants also form the basis of many items that we use in our day-to-day lives. A considerable amount of the furniture we use is made of wood and, of course, most of the varieties of paper we use come from the same source. Cotton and linen used to make clothes, bed linen and soft furnishings come from a plant. Plants are also used to make medicines, such as aspirin. Flavourings, smells and colours found in non-edible products such as toiletries are taken from plants, while other derivatives of plants have uses such as thickening ice cream.

Germination and growth

When a seed is planted, the process of germination is the start of a new plant growing from that seed. When a seed begins to germinate, this is not really the beginning of the seed's life because it had already started to grow and develop when it was maturing. In order to germinate, seeds need warmth and water. Seeds need particular conditions to germinate successfully. They can lie dormant for days or even years until the environmental conditions around them are suitable.

The process of germination begins when water is absorbed into the dry seed. This absorption of water causes the seed to swell and its outside coat (the testa) tears. The embryo inside the seed has been dormant since the seed left its parent plant. Nutrients that are stored in the seed are digested by enzymes (a type of protein that speeds up a chemical reaction) and carried to the embryo, which begins to grow.

As the plant begins to grow, the shoot grows upwards while the root grows downwards. The root draws water and nutrients from the soil. When the shoot emerges into sunlight, the plant becomes able to make its own food for growth, through photosynthesis. This is the sunlight-driven combining of water, carbon dioxide and chlorophyll (from the green leaves) to make food (glucose).

When growing seeds in a classroom, use seeds that germinate and grow quickly under favourable conditions so that the children don't get impatient waiting to see something happen. Seeds that grow quite rapidly are cress, sunflower and marrow. For the activities in the lesson plan it would be best to have the seeds already grown into seedlings so that the children will be able to see that they will grow some more and might have flowers.

Sow the seeds in good-quality soil, keep them in a warm place and water them regularly. (Don't let the soil dry out, but avoid drowning or water-logging the seedlings.) Germinated seedlings can be very fragile so must be treated with care. (**Safety:** be aware that many seeds bought from garden centres will have been treated with pesticides and should not be handled by children.)

Roots

A plant is made up of a root system and a shoot system. The roots of a plant penetrate the soil and absorb water and minerals. The root tips are covered with root hairs, which give the roots a greater surface area for absorption. Some plants have one major vertical root, called a 'taproot', with other smaller roots coming from it. Roots also anchor the plant firmly into the ground. Some taproots, such as carrots and parsnips, store food. The food stored in these roots is intended to feed the plant when it produces flowers and fruit, but we harvest the roots for food before this can happen.

Shoots

The shoot system of a plant is made up of stems, leaves and flowers. Where a leaf is attached to the stem (at a node), you can often see a bud (axillary bud). Another bud (terminal bud) at the end of the shoot will grow and the axillary buds remain dormant. If a terminal bud is removed (for example, by pruning), the axillary buds may begin to grow to produce new shoots or leaves.

Stems

The stem of a plant is usually tube-shaped. It transports water and nutrients around the plant as well as supporting leaves and flowers. Materials made by the leaves and materials absorbed by the roots are carried around the plant through thin tubes inside the stem.

Leaves

Leaves come in all shapes and sizes and are an important clue to telling one plant from another. Most leaves have a flattened surface (a blade) and are joined to the stem by a stalk (a petiole). Veins carry materials to and from the leaf while tiny holes (stomata) allow gases and water vapour in and out. The primary role of a leaf is to carry out photosynthesis (see above).

Flowers

The flower is the plant's reproductive organ. Before it opens, the delicate flower is protected by a set of sepals, which afterwards lie beneath the petals of the open flower. The petals of a flower vary greatly in shape, number and colour – they are often brightly coloured and/or scented for the purpose of attracting insects for pollination. The stamen is the male part of the flower and is composed of a tall filament on which sits a pollen-containing anther.

The female parts of the flower – the ovary (containing ovules or eggs), the style and the stigma – are often in the centre of the flower. The stigma is the sticky tip of the style, which is a tube-like structure leading down to the ovary. When a pollen grain (from the anther of another flower) reaches the stigma, it grows a pollen tube down to the ovule in the ovary. The ovule is fertilised and forms a seed.

Growing plants

LESSON PLAN

> **Science objectives (Unit 1B)**
> - To know that plants grow.
> - To make observations of plants.
> - To use drawings to record their observations and to communicate what happened.
> - To know that plants have leaves, stems and flowers.

Resources

- Seed trays and soil
- Packets of fast-growing seeds such as sunflower, cress or marrow
- Labels
- Water and a small watering can
- Pencils, scissors and glue
- Generic sheet 1 (page 19)
- Activity sheets 1–3 (pages 20–22)
- An OHP

Starting points: *whole class*

Show the children some seeds and ask them to think of words to describe them. Invite them to guess what plant the seeds come from and then show them the seed packet.

Tell the children that they are going to grow some plants. Using Generic sheet 1 on an OHP, draw the changes to the plant as it grows from the seed, and ask the children if they can name the parts of the plant that you are drawing (leaf, stem, roots, flower).

Discuss what the seeds will need to grow. Together plant some fast-growing seeds such as cress. (See safety note on page 15.) Put the seeds in a warm place and decide together how often you are going to water them. As they grow, ask the children to record their growth by drawing the different stages. How often they record the growth will depend on how quickly the plants are growing and changing.

While the seeds are growing remind the children of their responsibility in caring for them. They will need constant warmth and regular watering. The plants will be fragile in their early stages of growth, so they will need to be handled with care.

Group activities

Tell the children that they are going to look at the stages of plant growth.

Activity sheet 1
This sheet is aimed at children who need more support. They have to cut the pictures from this sheet and place them in the correct order before sticking them onto a piece of plain paper. They have to cut out the labels and label each picture. Then they have to label a flower and a leaf on one of the pictures, by cutting out the labels or by writing.

Activity sheet 2
This sheet is aimed at children who can work independently. They have to cut out and sequence four pictures. They have to label the pictures using the labels provided or by writing. Then they have to label leaves, flowers, roots and stems in the pictures.

Activity sheet 3
This sheet is aimed at more able children who can sequence five stages of a plant's growth. They have to label the leaves, flowers, roots and stems that they see. On the back of the sheet, with help from a word bank, they have to explain what is happening to the plant in each picture.

Plenary session

Ask the children to show their drawings of the growing seeds and ask some of them to explain what has happened to the seeds. Talk through what happened to the seed. (It took in water so its coat burst. The roots and shoots started to grow. It had two leaves. When it grew taller, it had many leaves.) Discuss what the adult plant will look like.

Ideas for support

Read the words on the activity sheet with the children.

Take photographs of each stage of the plants' growth and ask the children to practise sequencing the photographs. Ask them to make labels explaining what is happening to the plants in each picture. The photographs and labels could be used to make a class display or class book.

Ideas for extension

Ask the children to find out which plant the seeds you planted came from. Ask them to find out which part of a plant produces the seeds, and how the seeds are dispersed from the plant.

Give the children one or two different types of seeds to plant at home. (See safety note on page 15.) Remind them what plants need and see whether they can grow the plants into seedlings. They should make their own notes on the growth of the plants over a few weeks.

Over a period of time, go on to observe the growth of many different types of seeds, such as beans, peas, amaryllis and mung beans.

Linked ICT activities

Tell the children the story of 'Jack and the beanstalk'. Talk about what happened to the magic beans. Ask the children if they think that there really could be magic beans. Talk about what it would be like to grow magic flowers from magic seeds. Introduce the children to a graphics program; for example, 'Granada Colours', 'Fresco', 'Dazzle' or another similar graphics program.

Show the children how to use the paintbrush tools and the fill tool. Tell them that they are going to draw their own magic flowers. Encourage the children to use the different drawing tools to create their magic flowers. Print the flowers out and add them to a wall display of the story of 'Jack and the beanstalk'. Create a large paper beanstalk which winds its way around the classroom walls add the magic flowers to the magic beanstalk.

Growing plants

Predict what will happen to the seed.

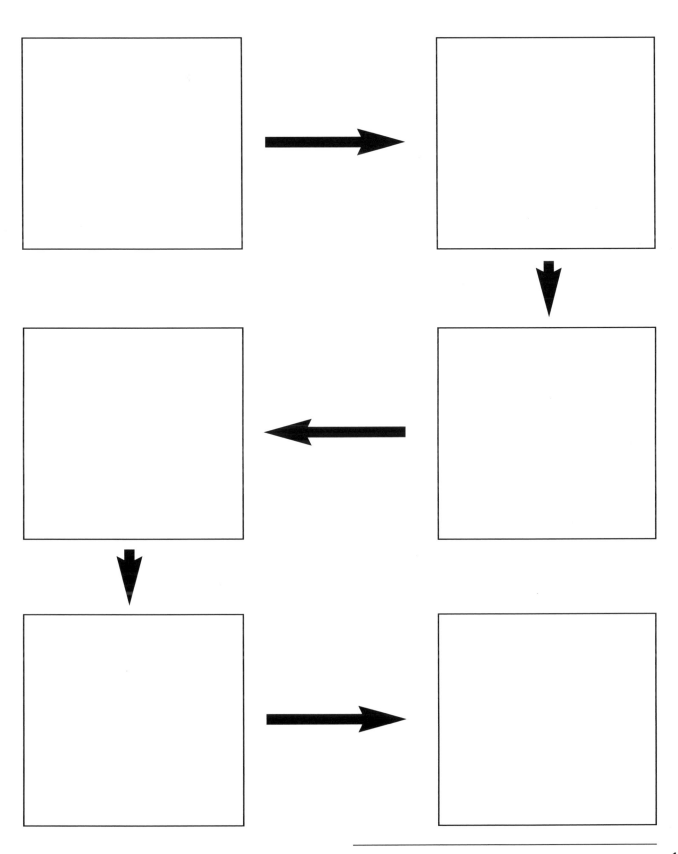

Name _____

Growing plants

Cut out these pictures. On another sheet of paper, stick them in the order in which they will happen when you plant a seed.

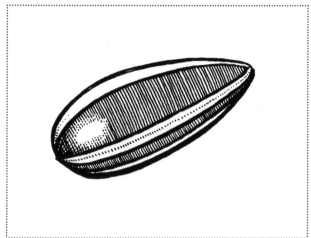

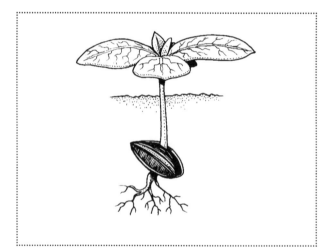

Cut out these labels and match them to the pictures.

seedling	adult plant	seed

Label a leaf and a flower that you can see in the pictures.

leaf	flower

Growing plants

Cut out these pictures. On another sheet of paper, stick them in the order in which they will happen when you plant a seed.

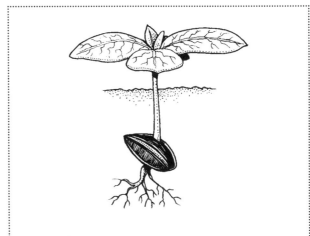

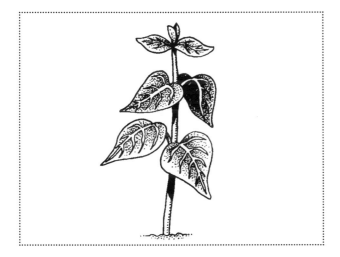

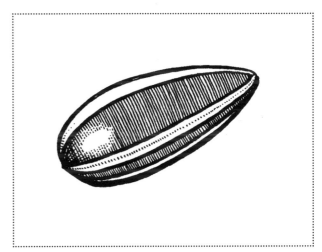

Cut out these labels and match them to the pictures.

| seedling | adult plant | seed | older seedling |

Label any leaves, flowers, roots and stems you can see in the pictures.

Name _____

Growing plants

Cut out these pictures. On another sheet of paper, stick them in the order in which they will happen when you plant a seed.

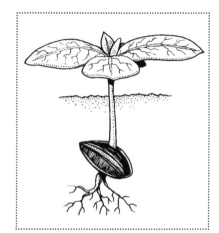

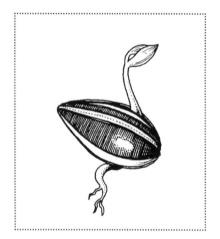

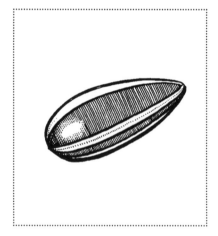

Label any leaves, flowers, roots and stems you can see in the pictures.

On the back of your sheet, explain what is happening in each picture. Use the word bank below to help you.

Word bank

seeds   root   shoot   seedling   young   adult
plant   grow   flower   leaf   stem

Plants as food

CHAPTER 3

TEACHERS' NOTES

Food providers

Plants are the primary providers of food for humans. It is currently recommended by the government that we eat five portions of fruit and vegetables per day to ensure that our bodies receive the vitamins, minerals and roughage they require. Most of our carbohydrate intake comes originally from plants, such as pasta, rice, couscous, potatoes and bread. In fact, most everyday foods – baked beans, cereal, orange juice – contain ingredients that originally come from a plant. When we use plants as a source of food we often don't eat the whole plant, just a specific part.

Leaves

The leaves of an edible plant are usually picked off, washed and used directly as a food source. They can vary in size from large cabbage leaves to small thyme leaves, and may be chosen for their crunchy texture, their appearance or their strong flavour. Green leaves are rich in vitamins and minerals. They also contain a significant amount of fibre, which helps to keep our digestive systems healthy. They contain only small amounts of fats and protein. Storing and cooking leaves can lower the level of vitamins such as vitamin C – with many vegetables, it is often healthier to eat them fresh and raw.

Stems

The stems of a plant are often overlooked as a source of food, although animals often devour the whole plant, stems and all. Leaves and fruit that are to be eaten are often picked off the stem and then the stem is discarded. Typical exceptions are celery and rhubarb, where the stem is eaten as the source of food. (**Safety:** note that the rhubarb leaf is poisonous.) The plant cells in a stem are often tougher than those in leaves, because the stem is designed to give the plant support. In an edible plant the stems are safe to eat, but their tough texture may not be to everyone's taste.

Seeds and nuts

Seeds are often used as a food source. Inside a seed is an embryonic component and a store of nutrients to feed the embryo if the seed were to germinate. This store is high in energy but is also often higher in fat than other parts of a plant. Beans such as runner beans and broad beans are seeds, and the bean pods are the plants' fruit. We usually eat runner bean pods, but not broad bean pods.

Nuts (apart from peanuts, which are leguminous plants similar to peas but whose pods grow underground) are the seeds of trees and are protected by a hard outer layer that we crack open to reveal the soft edible part inside.

Fruit

The fruits of some plants are dry, hard and spiky, and cannot be eaten, but the bright-coloured fleshy fruits of other plants provide healthy and often sweet-tasting food. A plant produces fruit to aid its seed dispersal. Seeds need to be dropped away from the parent plant and away from each other, to ensure that they are not competing for the same space, water and nutrients. They also need some protection during this process. The juicy, fleshy outer layer of the fruit builds up around maturing seeds. As the seeds ripen, so does the fruit. This means that when the fruit is ready to be eaten, the seeds are ready to be dispersed. The seeds have a protective coat to stop them being attacked by acids when they pass through the digestive system of an animal or a human. The fruit of a plant contains water, vitamins, natural sugars and other healthy nutrients. Fruits are low in fat (the exceptions being fruits such as avocados and olives).

Roots

The roots anchor the plant firmly into the ground and absorb water, nutrients and minerals. Some plants have a large taproot, with other smaller and finer roots branching off it. The taproot penetrates deep into the soil and acts as a store for carbohydrates that the plant produces. Underground is a good place to store food, where there is some protection from animals and the weather.

Perennial plants (plants that grow year after year) produce carbohydrates in the summer (by photosynthesis). Over the winter months, the carbohydrates are stored in the roots, ready for use in the spring when the plant grows new shoots but does not have enough leaves to produce food by photosynthesis.

Annual plants (those that only live for one year) produce carbohydrates by photosynthesis, but do not need to store the food for the following year.

Many of the plants that we use as food sources are root crops – sweet potatoes, swedes, turnips, carrots and parsnips. This store of carbohydrates that we eat provides us with low-fat and high-energy foods. Again, the plants are harvested before they have a chance to use the carbohydrates as a source of energy for shoot and flower growth.

Flowers

A flower is the reproductive structure of a plant. Although its role is to produce seeds, the fragrance, flavour and colour that the flower sometimes possesses make it an attractive source of food for many animals. Flowers are often used to garnish and decorate meals, but the flowers of many plants – daisy, marigold, dandelion, pansy and fuchsia – can be eaten safely by humans. But remember that any flowers to be eaten must be free of all pesticides and other chemicals. (Flowers bought from a florist are likely to have been treated with pesticides.)

Cultural differences

A wide variety of staple plant foods are used across the world. There are also many unusual ones – the dried buds of the tiger lily are often used in Chinese cooking, the leaf stalks of the water orchid are used in Thai soups and the tubers of the early purple orchid are eaten raw or made into sweets in India.

Plants as food

Science objectives (Unit 1B)
• To know that plants provide food for humans.

Resources
- Generic sheet 1 (page 27)
- Activity sheets 1–3 (pages 28–30)
- A collection of edible plants
- Labels – 'leaf', 'root', 'stem' and 'flower'
- Whiteboard
- Pens
- Sticky-tack

Starting points: *whole class*

Tell the children that they are going to find out about plants that are used for food. Cut out the pictures of foods from Generic sheet 1 and show them to the children. Ask them to help you sort them into two groups – those that come from plants and those that don't. Questions to ask are 'What is the plant called?' and 'Which plant does the food come from?' Look at the foods that do not come from plants and ask the children where those foods come from. Be aware that some children may not realise that meat comes from animals and may not be comfortable with this thought.

Show the children some plants that have an edible part. Draw up a chart on the board, with the headings: 'skin', 'flesh', 'leaves', 'stem', 'root' and 'seeds'. Give the children a list of edible plants such as apple, tomato, pepper, carrot, cabbage, sweet potato, celery and okra. Ask them to say which columns each plant belongs in (apple – skin and flesh; tomato – skin, flesh and seeds; pepper – skin and flesh; carrot – root; cabbage – leaves; sweet potato – root; celery – stem and leaves; okra – skin, flesh and seeds).

Group activities

Tell the children that they are going to look at the edible parts of some plants.

Activity sheet 1
This sheet is aimed at children who need more support. They can recognise which part of a plant they would eat, such as the fruit from an apple tree.

They have to colour the edible parts of some food plants. On the back of the sheet, they have to draw and label three more food plants.

Activity sheet 2
This sheet is aimed at children who can work independently. They can recognise which part of a plant they would eat and can name that part of the plant as a leaf, stem, root, fruit or flower. They have to colour and label the edible parts of some food plants. On the back of the sheet, they have to draw and name a food made from each of three plants.

Activity sheet 3
This activity sheet is aimed at more able children. They have to draw plants of which the roots, leaves, flowers, seeds, stems or fruit are eaten. They have to suggest which plants are used to make common foods – bread (wheat or rye), crisps (potatoes) and chocolate (cocoa tree).

Plenary session

Ask the children to help you make a list on the board of all the foods that we could not eat if we didn't have plants around us. Encourage them to see that many foods, including favourites such as chocolate, crisps, chips and pizza, could not be eaten if there were no plants.

Ideas for support

Help the children to read the words on the sheet.

Work with them to differentiate between the different parts of a plant and identify which parts we eat in each case.

With the children cut out pictures of foods from magazines and encourage the children to sort them into foods that come from plants and foods that don't. Also use these pictures to make a display for the classroom, labelling the parts of the plants that we eat.

Ideas for extension

Ask the children to find out what plants are grown for making baked beans, pasta and raisins.

Linked ICT activities

Talk to the children about different types of fruit and vegetables. Make a chart using pictures of fruit and vegetables, starting with fruit the children will recognise, such as a banana, an apple and an orange. Display the pictures on the wall and ask the children to write their names underneath their favourite fruit.

Using a simple data sorting program, such as 'Counter for Windows', enter the names of the favourite fruits into a list. Working with the whole class, ask the children which their favourite fruit is. Look at the pictures that are on display and check the children's names against the pictures. Count the names by each fruit and add them to the list on the program. This program will allow you to see the information as a graph and as a pie chart.

Once the information has been entered, look at it in a graph format and ask the children questions such as 'Which is the most popular fruit?' and 'Which is the least popular?'

Plants as food

Name _____

Plants as food

Look at these plants. Colour in the parts that we eat.

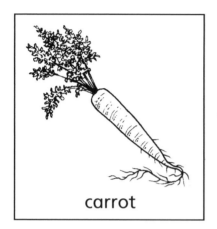

carrot

apple

wheat

sweetcorn

spinach

tomato

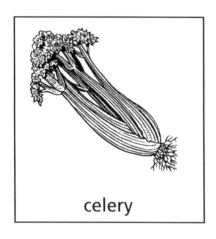

celery

broccoli

swede

On the back of this sheet, draw three more food plants.
Write the names of the foods on your pictures.

Name _____

Plants as food

Colour in the parts of these plants that we eat. Then label each edible part. Use the word bank below to help you.

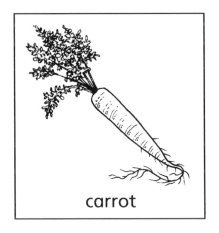

carrot

apple

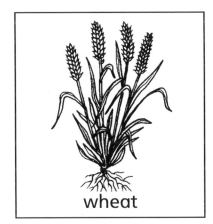

wheat

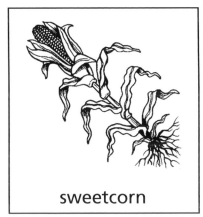

sweetcorn

spinach

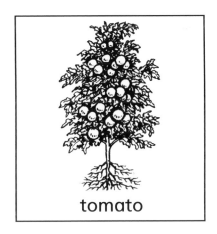

tomato

celery

broccoli

swede

Word bank

leaf   stem   root   fruit   flower

On the back of this sheet, draw and name a food you might eat that is made from each of these plants: tomato, potato, wheat.

Plants as food

Read the label under each box. Think of a plant where we eat that part and draw it in the box.

root	leaf	flower
fruit	seed	stem

Which plants are used to make these foods?

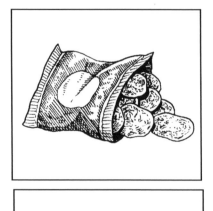

Water and plants

TEACHERS' NOTES

Plants need water to grow. Some plants need a large amount of water to grow healthily, but others can survive on a very small amount of water. Plants rely on water to carry out a number of essential processes, but how does a regular supply of water enter the plant?

Transpiration

Plants draw up water from their surroundings by the process of transpiration. Water evaporates continuously from leaves through tiny surface holes (stomata). As water leaves the plant in this way, it is replaced by water that has been taken in through the root system and transported up through the stem. Water travels from the roots to the leaves through tube-shaped cells (xylem – pronounced 'zylem'). Xylem cells are dead cells that are woody, so they support the plant as well as providing a structure for water transport.

Within cells anywhere in the plant there is a continuous movement of water. The measure of whether water is more likely to move to one place or another is known as the water potential of a cell. As changes in 'water potential' take place – such as when solutes (dissolved particles) are added or there is a change in air pressure – water inside the cells automatically moves from a place where the water potential is higher to a place where it is lower. This causes the movement of water between individual cells and also from one part of a plant to another. The water is transported as xylem sap, which also includes other minerals and nutrients taken up by the roots.

As water is lost by evaporation through the stomata in the leaves, the cells surrounding the stomata become dry, their water potential becomes lower and so water from neighbouring cells with a higher water potential moves into them. This chain of water movement from cell to cell in the leaf continues until eventually water is taken from the xylem sap. As the water moves from the xylem sap it creates a pull of sap upwards. This pull occurs all the way along from the tip of the shoot system down to the tip of the roots. As this loss of water lowers the water potential in the cells of the root

tips, water flows in from the surrounding soil. The chains of water molecules that bond and form are very strong. As long as no breaks in the molecule chain occur, the flow of water up from the soil into the xylem cells, up into the shoot system of the plant and out via the stomata, remains continuous.

Support

Water itself is essential in providing support for a growing plant. When a plant cell is filled with water it is described as being turgid. Many plants rely on their cells continuously maintaining a turgid state so that the upper leaves and shoots remain supported and in the correct position with which to photosynthesise to their full potential. If for some reason the cells in a plant lose water, they shrivel and the cell is described as being limp or 'flaccid'. A plant that has flaccid cells will wilt and lose the ability to support itself.

Plant cell growth

Water also plays an important role in plant cell growth. Although plant cells do divide to make new plant cells, much of the visible growth of roots and shoots occurs due to the uptake of water into a plant cell. As water enters a plant cell, the cell wall stretches and the cell grows larger. When the plant cell stops taking in water and therefore stops growing, a more permanent material is deposited around the cell wall to make the growth permanent.

Photosynthesis

Water is essential for the vital process of photosynthesis. The plant uses the Sun's energy to split water into oxygen, which is released by the plant, and hydrogen, which is then used to convert carbon dioxide (from the air) into carbohydrates that provide the plant with food and other structural materials. Without water the process would not be able to take place and the plant would be without food. Most of the photosynthesis that occurs takes place in the leaves, so if there is a shortage of water in the leaves then the rate of photosynthesis will be greatly reduced. As well as its importance for photosynthesis, a steady supply of water to the leaves ensures that they are supported and maintained at an angle that allows them to catch the sunlight. So wilting leaves, lacking water in their cells, are not able to absorb the sunlight to their full potential.

Adaptations to water in the environment

In the table below are some examples of plants that can live in very wet environments, environments where there is a regular water supply, and in very dry environments.

Watery environments	Regular supply of water	Dry environments
Common arrowhead Water lily Canadian pondweed Aquatic buttercup	Daisy Hosta Thyme Daffodil	Marram grass Cactus Pine tree Holly tree

In an environment where water is in plentiful supply, such as in a pond, plants adapt in specific ways to cope with this. For a normal plant, such as a house plant, a continuous supply of water may cause the roots of the plant to rot, but water-loving plants flourish even after sitting in the water all day. The leaves of plants that float on water do not contain as many supporting cells, because the water supports the plants. They often have air chambers, which help the plant to float.

Plants that grow in very dry (arid) conditions where water is scarce, have adapted to minimise the loss of water from the plant. They often also have the ability to store a supply of water for later use. Plants such as cacti have what are known as 'succulent' leaves. The leaves are thick and fleshy and are shaped to reduce their surface area and therefore the area that could lose water to the atmosphere. Other plants that grow in arid conditions often have leaves that are tightly packed together to help to minimise water loss. Plants such as pine trees and holly have a waxy cuticle covering their leaves to help prevent water loss.

Adaptations to drought

In conditions when a normal water supply suddenly becomes scarce, plants can make some adaptations to protect themselves from dehydration. The tiny holes in the leaves (stomata) can close and the plant may stop growing any more new leaves.

Water and plants

LESSON PLAN

Science objectives (Unit 1B)
- To make careful observations of the plants and to record these in a simple chart or table provided for them.
- To conclude that plants need water to grow.
- To know that plants have roots.
- To observe and compare the roots of different plants.

Resources
- Generic sheets 1–3 (pages 35–37)
- Activity sheets 1–3 (pages 38–40)
- Seedlings or a plant
- Two trays of fast-growing seedlings (large enough to be clearly seen), such as cress
- Water and a small watering can
- Plastic cups as water measures
- Coloured pens
- Labels – 'Being watered' and 'No water'
- Pot-bound plant
- Fork
- Larger pot
- Soil
- Collection of plants to show various shapes and sizes of roots

Starting points: *whole class*

Before the day of the lesson, show the seedlings (or plant) to the children. Leave them without water for a few days and then show them to the children again. Ask the children to describe them now. Each time you show the seedlings, record what they look like. Prompt the children to see that they have wilted and look unhealthy. Ask them to suggest a way in which they can make the seedlings grow healthy again. If they do not suggest watering, invite one of them to look more closely at the soil and to touch it.

Use an enlarged copy of Generic sheet 1 and coloured pens to show the children the path water takes through the plant. Explain why the plant needs water and what it does with it. (Needs water for healthy growth. Draws up water through the roots. Water fills plant cells to keep the stem and leaves supported. Water works in the leaves, with sunlight, to make food for the plant.)

Tell the children they are going to test some plants to see how important water is to them. Ask them to think of a way to set up an experiment to prove that plants need water to grow healthily. Using their ideas, discuss the investigation they are going to carry out. Write what they are going to do on a sheet of paper and display it in the classroom next to the plants that are being grown, to remind them what they are trying to find out.

Provide two trays of seedlings that are large enough to be observed clearly. Clearly label the seedlings that are being watered and those being left without water.

Decide who will water the plants, when they will water them, and how much water they will give them. Record these decisions for the children on Generic sheet 2 and display the sheet next to the plants. After each interval, show the plants to the children and ask them to record what they see. They can do this individually, in groups or in pairs.

Tell the children that they are going to look at the roots of plants. Show them a collection of plants that have varying types and sizes of roots. Show them Generic sheet 3. Look at each plant in turn and discuss the roots that can be seen and their differences. Point out that the seedling has only a few roots compared with the others because it is the youngest plant.

The pot plant's roots are very compact and intertwined and have been pushed close together because of the limitation of room in the pot.

The tree's roots are spread very wide and they grow further out than its branches to prevent the tree from falling over.

The roots of the carrot are fine and are present all over the carrot, not just its end.

The rose bush has shallower roots than the tree but again they are widespread to give the plant stability.

The banyan tree has roots that are visible above the soil. They grow down from the outstretched branches in order to support them.

Show the children a plant that has outgrown its pot. Ask them why they think it needs repotting. Show them the tightly packed roots, which have become entangled as they have run out of space to grow. Demonstrate how to repot the plant, explaining that the roots need more space to search for water and nutrients. If, while you gently untangle some of the roots with a fork, some of them tear, then more will grow in their place.

Group activities

Tell the children that they are going to predict the effect of water on plants.

Activity sheet 1
This sheet is aimed at children who need more support. They have to choose what the plant will look like if it has been given no water, one drop of water or a good sprinkle of water. They have to show this by ticking the correct options. Then they have to say how to make a wilted plant look healthy again.

Activity sheet 2
This sheet is aimed at children who can work independently. They have to predict what will happen when a plant is given no water, a drop of water or a good sprinkle of water. They have to record their predictions by drawing the results they would expect to see. Then they have to write a word or two to describe how the plant will be (healthy, wilted or very wilted).

Activity sheet 3
This sheet is aimed at more able children. They have to explain what has happened in the pictures. Encourage them to say whether the plant looks healthy or wilted. They have to explain (simply) why. (The plant has wilted because it does not have enough water.)

Plenary session

Discuss the children's results from the investigation and help them to conclude what they have found out about plants and water. Look again at the wilted seedlings. Ask the children to suggest a way of reviving the plants. Give the plants some water. Look at the plants over a period of days (keep up the watering) to see if they begin to look healthy again.

Ideas for support

Support the language needed – 'healthy' and 'wilted'. Talk with the children about the 'some water but not enough' situation for the plant.

Take some photographs of plants in the school grounds at different times of the year. Compare photographs of plants taken in hot dry weather and those taken in cold wet weather.

Give some children in the class the responsibility of watering any plants in the classroom. As they are watering them, ask questions to reinforce why they are watering and what may happen to the plants if they do not do their job properly.

Ideas for extension

Ask the children to find out how plants stay healthy when they live in an area like the desert, where it is hot and dry and there is very little water.

Linked ICT activities

Talk to the children about what they have found out about plants needing water to live. Using a simple word processing program, such as 'Talking Write Away' or 'Textease', help them to think of some sentences that describe what plants need to stay alive and what experiments they carried out to show this.

If there is a projector with a large screen, work with the whole class to enter the text and read it as it is typed in. If it is not possible to use a large screen, work with small groups of children to carry out the same activity.

Water and plants

Water and plants

This chart will help us to remember to water the plants properly.

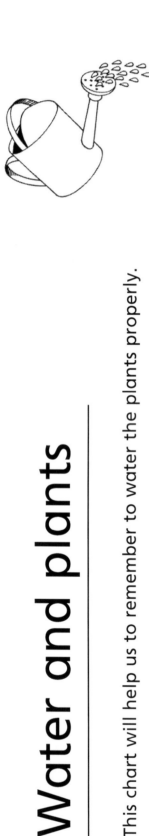

Name of person watering			
Day			
How much water	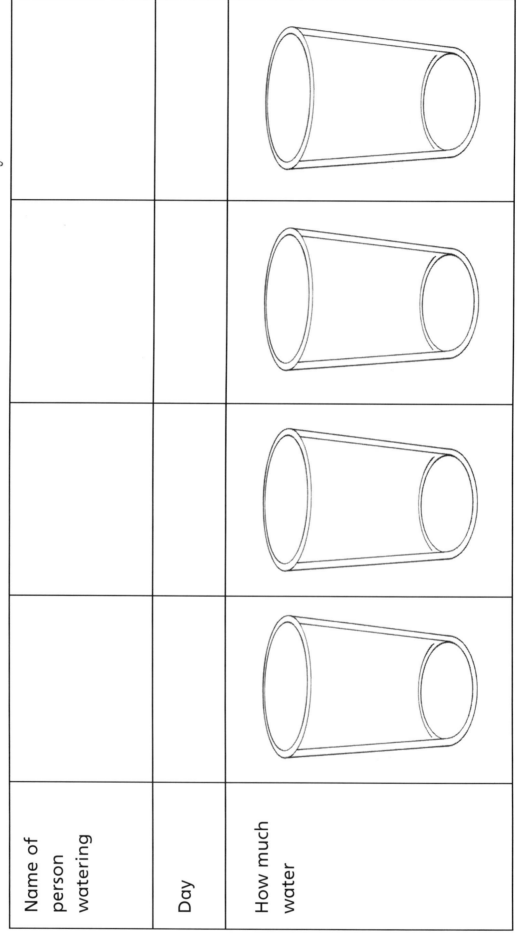		

Water and plants

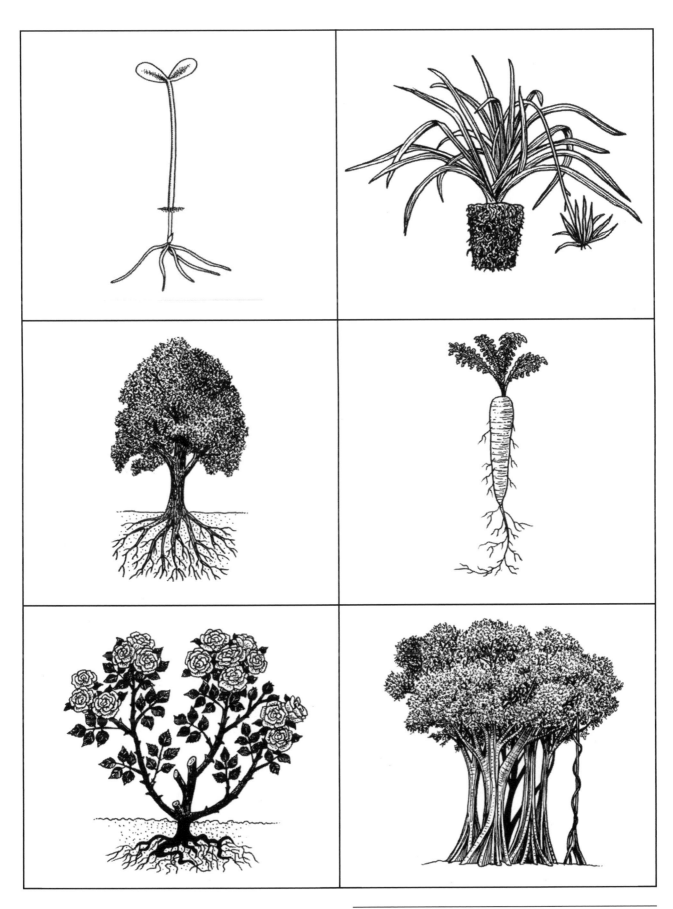

Name _____

Water and plants

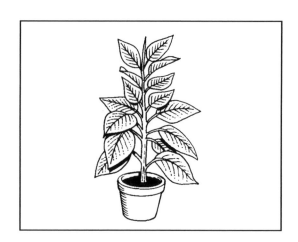

What will happen to this plant if we:

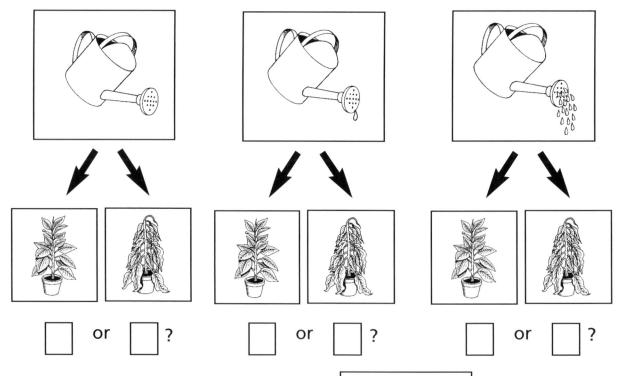

☐ or ☐ ?   ☐ or ☐ ?   ☐ or ☐ ?

What could we give this plant
to make it more healthy?

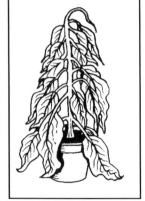

Name _____

Water and plants

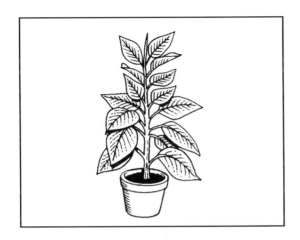

Word bank
leaf
stem
wilt
grow tall

Draw what will happen to this plant if we:

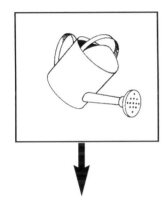

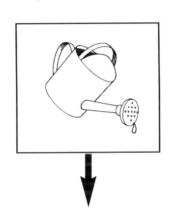

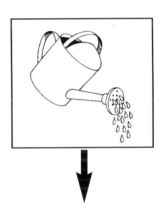

Draw the plants here. Label your pictures.

This plant will

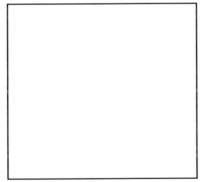

This plant will

This plant will

Name _____

Water and plants

Explain what has happened.

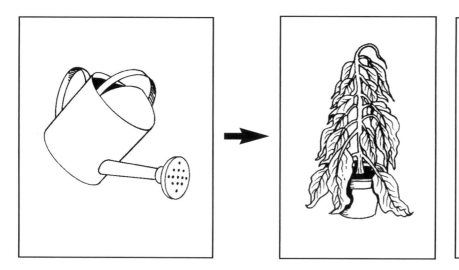

This plant looks like this because

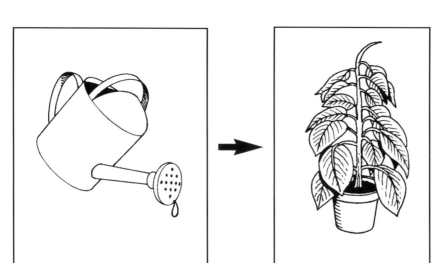

This plant looks like this because

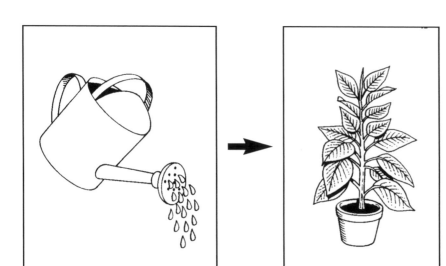

This plant looks like this because

Plants and light

CHAPTER 5

TEACHERS' NOTES

Green plants depend on light to grow healthily. If the source of light is removed, they may continue to grow for a while but will look increasingly unhealthy and will eventually die.

Photosynthesis

Photosynthesis is the process by which plants produce the food they need to survive. In the presence of light, plants use carbon dioxide (from the air) and water (drawn in by transpiration) to produce carbohydrates and oxygen. Sunlight provides the energy that a plant needs to fuel the chemical reactions in the process. Without sunlight, photosynthesis would not take place.

Plant cells contain specialised components (organelles) called 'chloroplasts', which have the ability to harvest energy from light. Chloroplasts contain a green pigment called 'chlorophyll', which gives a plant its green colour. Chloroplasts are found in nearly all of a plant's cells, but the majority of photosynthesis takes place in the leaves. The water that is needed is transported through the tube-shaped xylem cells. The carbon dioxide needed from the air around the plant enters the leaf through the tiny surface holes (stomata).

The process

The first step in the process of photosynthesis is the conversion of light energy to chemical energy. The chlorophyll present in the chloroplast cells absorbs the light from the Sun, splitting water molecules into oxygen and hydrogen. The oxygen is released into the air as a gas, leaving the leaf through the stomata in the leaves.

The second step involves hydrogen undergoing further complex chemical reactions and converting carbon dioxide into carbohydrates for the plant to use as a food source.

Phototropism

Light is such an important factor for healthy growth that plants have the ability to adapt their growth pattern according to the position of light in the environment. This growth response is called 'phototropism'. It can be seen clearly if a plant is placed in a position where light comes from just one direction – the plant will grow towards the light. If the plant is then turned around, it will begin to grow towards the light again. Plants that grow away from a light source are said to have negative phototropism.

Early experiments on this type of growth response were carried out by Charles Darwin and his son Francis. They discovered that a plant would only grow towards the light if the tip of the shoot was present. They also worked out that the bend in the plant takes place further down the shoot and that some sort of message is carried from the tip of the plant down to these cells, causing them to bend.

Chlorosis

If plants are grown in the absence of light then they become chlorotic and develop what is known as 'chlorosis'. The leaves will lose their green colour and become yellow in appearance. Growth will be slower and the plants will generally look unhealthy. Chlorosis occurs because in the absence of light the plant chlorophyll (the green pigment) degrades.

Plant adaptations

Different plant species need different amounts of sunlight to photosynthesise and produce the food they need. Some plants thrive only in direct sunlight, while some need only partial sunlight and others grow better in shady conditions. The structure of a plant is designed to enable it to carry out the level of photosynthesis it needs. The flat, thin shape of leaves makes it easy for the cells to absorb the light and gases they need, while the stems are designed to transport water and other necessary nutrients to the leaf. Stems also help to support and position the leaves to ensure that they are able to receive the light that they need.

The rays produced by the Sun can be very hot, especially in the summer months. Just like humans and animals, plants can get sunburnt and, as with humans, it is the UVB rays that cause damage to the plant's cells.

In the table below are examples of some plants that can live in direct sunlight, some that are shade lovers and some that require partial shade.

Direct sunlight	Partial shade	Shade
Ox-eye daisy	Hollyhock	Foxglove
Oak tree	Marigold	Snowdrop
Poppy	Snapdragon	Crocus
Oil-seed rape	Busy Lizzie	Bluebell

Plants and light

Science objectives (Unit 1B)
- To turn ideas about whether green plants need light to grow into a form that can be tested.
- To observe and compare green plants grown in light and dark places.
- To conclude that green plants need light to grow well.
- To know that plants are living but that an artificial plant is not living.

Resources

- Generic sheets 1 and 2 (pages 45 and 46)
- Activity sheets 1–3 (pages 47–49)
- Potted plants (two for each group of children)
- Dark cupboard
- Sticky tape
- Water and a small watering can
- Plastic cups as water measures
- Potted plant and similar artificial plant
- Labels – 'real plant', 'artificial plant', 'water me', 'give me light' and 'keep me in the dark'

Starting points: *whole class*

Remind the children that plants need water to grow and ask them if they can suggest anything else that plants need. Prompt them to consider whether or not plants need light. Look at any plants inside the classroom or out in the school grounds. Are the plants getting light as they grow?

Tell the children that they are going to do an experiment that will take around two weeks, to see how light affects plants. Ask them to think of a way to set up an experiment to test whether or not plants will grow without light. Using their ideas, discuss the investigation they are going to carry out. Write what they are going to do on Generic sheet 1. Discuss whether or not they will water the plants, where the plants will be kept, and when they will look at the plants. Ask the children to predict what will happen to the plants.

Give each group of children two of the same kind of plant. Read the labels 'water me', 'give me light' and 'keep me in the dark' with the children. Ask them to stick the labels onto the plant pots. This will help to introduce the idea of a fair test to them and remind them that they just want to find out the effect that light or lack of light has on the plant.

Put half the plant pots in a warm place in the classroom and the rest in a warm dark cupboard, and water them regularly. Decide who is going to water them, how much and how often. Record these decisions on Generic sheet 2 and display the sheet near the plants. Look at the plants on days 3, 8 and 14 (or the nearest if these fall over a weekend).

Group activities

Tell the children that they are going to record what happens during their tests on the plants.

Activity sheet 1
This sheet is aimed at children who need more support. They have to record differences between the plants by colouring pictures accordingly. They have to conclude their findings by choosing two things (from a list) that they feel they have found out from their investigation.

Activity sheet 2
This sheet is aimed at children who can work independently. They have to record their findings from the investigation by colouring pictures and drawing pictures of their own, to show the changes they observed. They have to complete a single-sentence conclusion (using a word bank) about what they found out from their investigation.

Activity sheet 3
This sheet is aimed at more able children. They have to draw a series of pictures to record the differences they observed in their investigation. They have to form their own conclusion about whether or not plants need light to grow well. They may need help to write their ideas down.

Plenary session

When the experiment is finished, discuss the outcome of the investigation. Ask the children to describe the appearance of each of the plants. Ask them how healthy each plant looks.

Reinforce the outcome as being that green plants need light to grow well. See if the children can suggest why plants need light. Then explain to them briefly that plants use the sunlight to make food.

Put two similar potted plants – one artificial and one real – on a table in front of the children. Ask 'Do you think that both of these plants need light to grow?' Next stick labels on the plants that read 'real plant' and 'artificial plant'. Ask 'Do you still think that they both need light to grow?' Discuss the differences between the plants and how to tell that one of them is not living. (Growing/not growing; needs water/doesn't need water; roots/no roots; needs light/doesn't need light.)

Show the children a plant that is dead. Ask them to explain what the difference is between this and the real plant and the artificial one. Can the dead one be brought back to life?

Ideas for support

Create a word bank with vocabulary you have introduced in the classroom. Display it where the children can see it when they are working.

Read Activity sheet 1 with the children.

Bring in a collection of plants, some of which have had less light than the others in the last few days. Show the children the plants and ask them if they think they look healthy. If they say no, see if they can tell you what might be wrong with them and what they could do to make them grow healthily again.

Ideas for extension

Ask the children if they can find out the name of a plant that loves to grow in the sunlight and one that doesn't like the sunlight but likes to grow in the shade. The children's suggestions could be displayed, with pictures, in the classroom.

Linked ICT activities

Show the children a photograph of a plant that has been grown without sunlight for a few weeks. Explain to them that a friend of yours has sent you the photograph to see if you can help them to understand what has happened to their plant and if you can help them to make it healthy again. The children could write letters on the computer to your friend explaining why the plant looks like it does and suggesting ways in which your friend can help the plant to grow healthy again, such as putting it in a place where it is sunny.

Take in some dried or fresh sunflowers (depending on the time of year) to show the children. Ask them why they think they are called sunflowers and where they think sunflowers grow. Show them some sunflower seeds and from the knowledge they already have, talk about how the flowers have grown from the seeds.

Show the children Van Gogh's sunflowers and, using a graphics program, such as 'Fresco', 'Granada Colours' or 'Dazzle', show them how to use the paint and spray tool to create their own sunflowers, using the same colours as in the Van Gogh painting.

Plants and light

How can we find out if plants need light to grow well?

What will we do?

What will we need?

Where will we keep the plants?

Will we water the plants?

How will we record what we see?

Water and plants

This chart will help us to remember to water the plants properly.

Day	1	3	5	7	9	11	13
Name of person watering							
How much water							

Name _____

Plants and light

Colour the plants to show what happened to them in your investigation.

	Day 1	Day 3	Day 8	Day 14
Water and light				
Water and no light				

Tick two things that you have found out.

Plants like sunbathing. ☐

Plants need light to grow healthy. ☐

Without light, plant leaves turn yellow. ☐

Plants are afraid of the dark. ☐

Plants and light

Colour and draw plants to show what happened in your investigation.

	Day 1	Day 3	Day 8	Day 14
Water and light				
Water and no light				

Complete the sentence. Use the word bank to help you.

We found out that plants _____

> **Word bank**
>
> light   grow   need   well

Name _____

Plants and light

Colour and draw plants to show what happened in your investigation.

	Day 1	Day 3	Day 8	Day 14
Water and light				
Water and no light				

What did your investigation show?

We found out that _____

Word bank: green, healthy

CHAPTER 6

Plants and animals around us

The plants and animals that you see when you go for a walk in your local environment will depend on the sort of area that you live in. For example, coastal regions may have different species from inland regions because plants and animals there may have special adaptations to living in the more salty conditions. Taking children on a walk around the school grounds, to a local park or another safe area will give them an idea of the sort of plants and animals that live right on their doorstep. See guidelines for walks on page 7.

Plant adaptations

Your immediate environment will be made up of many different habitats (places where organisms live). Different plants and animals live in different habitats and there are many reasons for this.

- The habitat must provide a suitable source of food and water.

- Animals have different dietary requirements and may not survive if there is not a steady source of an appropriate food available.

- Plants also have specific mineral requirements from the soil. Some plants will only grow in a certain type of soil because of the minerals it contains or lacks.

- Some animals may choose a specific habitat to protect themselves from predators. For example, birds may make their nests high up in the trees to ensure that foxes do not eat their eggs.

Where an animal or plant is adapted to live may also be affected by the amount of sunlight or shelter they want. Some plants, such as poppies, flourish in a sunny position, while others, such as bluebells, require shady, damp conditions to grow healthily. Most animals will choose a place to sleep where it is dark and sheltered from the elements. When active, some animals, such as butterflies, travel around in the warm sunlight, while others, such as slugs and woodlice, prefer to spend their time in areas where it is dark and damp.

The physiology of plants and animals may also affect their choice of habitats. Birds can fly to high places such as rooftops and trees, while snails are best suited to ground-level places where they can move slowly over a damp surface using their muscular foot. Ivy can climb over buildings and walls, while other plants, such as cranberry, remain at ground level and grow horizontally.

Plants and animals in your local environment

Here are some examples of the sorts of plants and animals that you may see as you walk around your local environment. Some of the animals may live in more than one type of place and others you may not see at all in your area.

Trees

If you study your local environment, the plants you may see in abundance are trees. Naturalised trees that have been there for many years may be found at your local park or on local grassland. The school grounds may contain trees that have been planted only recently. The variety of local trees will vary, but some common species are oak, ash, pine, sycamore and beech. Trees themselves provide a habitat for a variety of animals, including insects such as beetles and spiders. Larger animals such as squirrels make their home in tree trunks, while birds such as wood pigeons and mistlethrushes are commonly seen nesting in tree branches, and blue tits in holes in trees. Plants such as mosses and lichens will grow on the bark of trees and ivy may be found spiralling up the tree trunk.

Hedges

Hedges are commonly found in the local environment as they make an ideal border to partition one area from another. Species of hedges vary, with some common ones being privet and hawthorn. Hedges provide a dark, damp habitat ideal for slugs, snails and also insects such as beetles, woodlice, centipedes and earwigs. Some birds such as the garden warbler, blackbird, song thrush and long-tailed tit, will nest in hedges and eat the berries that grow there. Hedgehogs and mice also shelter underneath hedges. Plants such as brambles and dog roses may climb and grow up the hedges, and flowers such as the primrose may grow at the base of the hedge where it is sheltered.

Flowering plants

Flowering plants provide a habitat for a vast variety of insects. Flowers are visited regularly by butterflies, bees and wasps searching for nectar, while the leaves provide food and shelter for insects such as ladybirds, ants, spiders, beetles and flies.

On and under stones

A variety of mosses and lichens often cover stones. Underneath a stone where it is damp and dark you will find insects such as earwigs, spiders, woodlice and beetles, often with larger animals such as worms and slugs as well.

On walls or fences

Greater bindweed is one plant that has the ability to grow up a wall, and some species such as a plant called pellitory-of-the-wall will grow in cracks in walls. Mosses and lichens are commonly seen growing on wall surfaces, and insects such as spiders may also shelter in any cracks that are present. Wooden structures such as fencing may be inhabited by beetles, such as the deathwatch beetle, and red ants.

In grass

Grass is the home of many small animals and many varieties of plants. The grass itself is made up of many different species – some common ones may be lawn grass and rye grass. Daisies, buttercups, dandelions, nettles, dock and ribwort plantains are common plants that live in grassy areas. Small animals found here include grass snakes, worms, mice and hedgehogs as well as a multitude of insects, such as grasshoppers, beetles, flies, earwigs and centipedes.

Underground

Many animals live underground out of sight. If you are not lucky enough to see them you may still know they inhabit a site by the evidence they leave. Rabbit holes are often seen on hilly land and moles will leave molehills above ground, from the earth they have dug out of their tunnels. Badgers live in underground sets that may leave a large hole in the ground. The earth underground is also teeming with insects such as ants, spiders and beetles.

Treating the environment and animals with care

When children find plants and animals it is important that they do not touch them or try to pick them up. Before you leave for the walk, remind the children of this. Ask them to suggest why the plants and animals that they find should be left alone. Make sure that all adults who come on the walk are aware of this instruction as well.

On the walk you may need to turn over stones and logs to see the animals that can be found living there. Explain to the children that any object that you move will be put back afterwards, because it may be the animals' home and you don't want to leave the animals without somewhere to live. Small animals such as insects are also delicate – picking them up could hurt them and would definitely frighten them. Help the children to understand that they can learn a lot about an animal by watching it. There is no need for them to pick it up or to try to take it back into the classroom.

Some plants are poisonous or can cause an allergic reaction, and delicate leaves and petals may be damaged by touch. If picked, plants will eventually die. Remind the children that the plant may be a home for animals and that they will not learn anything more about the plant by holding it, so they should leave it growing where it is.

Hazards in working with soil

Working with soil is potentially hazardous.

- There can be hidden particulate matter embedded in the soil, such as glass, sharp stones or sharp pieces of wood. Wearing gardening gloves will protect your hands from these things. If children are to be looking closely at soil, they could move it with a gardening fork or even a kitchen fork and then, if necessary, an adult wearing gloves could actually touch the soil.

- Bacteria and parasites can regularly be found in soil due to the decay of dead plant and animal matter. Animals such as dogs and cats defecate in the soil. On the walk, try to avoid areas likely to be contaminated by animal faeces.

Hands must be thoroughly washed after any activity involving soil.

Plants and animals around us

> ## Science objectives (Unit 2B)
> • To know that there are different kinds of plants and animals in the immediate environment.
> • To treat animals and the environment with care and sensitivity.
> • To recognise hazards in working with soil.
> • To observe and make a record of animals and plants found.

Resources

- Generic sheets 1–3 (pages 54–56)
- Activity sheets 1–3 (pages 57–59)
- A plan or map of the local area
- Clipboards
- Pencils

Starting points: *whole class*

Introduce the term 'local environment' to the children and explain to them that this is the place around the school (or where we live). On the board draw a simple plan of the school and the grounds around it and extend the plan to include nearby parks or other places where you can take the children to look for plants and animals. A printed plan of the local area would be useful.

Tell the children that they are going to find out which plants and animals live in the local environment. Ask them to suggest where plants and animals might be found. On the plan on the board, shade in these places. Reinforce that plants and animals live in all sorts of places and not just in grassy areas. You may find that nearly all the map becomes shaded, helping to emphasise to the children that plants and animals are all around us.

Cut out the pictures from Generic sheet 1 and show them to the children one at a time. Ask them if they think they might see these animals in the local environment. Show them the pictures from Generic sheet 2 one at a time. Ask them if they think that they might see these plants in the place they are going to visit. Encourage them to give reasons for their answers.

Fieldwork

Tell the children that you are going to take them on a walk in the local environment. Show them where, on the plan.

Before you leave for the walk, remind the children of the importance of not touching the plants and animals they see. Emphasise that:

- delicate leaves and petals may be damaged by touching;
- picked plants will die;
- plants may be homes for animals;
- small animals are delicate – picking them up could hurt and frighten them;
- the children should not touch soil – it might be contaminated with microbes or animal droppings, or contain broken glass or sharp stones.

Give each child a clipboard, a pencil and a copy of Generic sheet 3. Read and explain the sheet to them.

Group activities

Tell the children they are going to draw pictures of what they saw on the walk in the local environment.

Activity sheet 1

This sheet is aimed at children who need more support. They have to choose words from the word bank that describe the place they visited. They have to draw one plant and one animal that they found there. They have to draw an animal they would find under a stone (earwig or woodlouse) and a plant that would grow in the grass (dandelion or daisy).

Activity sheet 2

This sheet is aimed at children who can work independently. They have to choose words from the word bank that describe the place they visited. They also have to add two words of their own. They have to draw one animal and one plant they saw in the environment. Then they have to draw a picture of where they found it. They also have to choose a word to describe each place.

Activity sheet 3

This sheet is aimed at more able children. They have to describe the place they visited, using their own key words. They have to draw a picture of one plant and one animal they found there. Then they have to draw the places where they found them, and suggest why the animal and plant live there.

Plenary session

Begin the plenary session by showing the children a blank chart such as the one below.

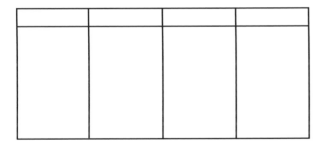

Ask them to suggest headings for the places where they found the different animals, such as grassy, woody and shady. Write these in the chart. You may need to add more columns for all the different places they think of.

woody	shady	grassy	

Ask the children to talk about one plant or animal they found on their walk. They need to tell their classmates where they found it – for example, under a stone – and why they think it lives there. As they feed back their information, add it to the chart.

Ideas for support

With the children, read all the names of the plants and animals on Generic sheets 1 and 2.

Take photographs of the plants and animals that you see in the local environment and display them in the classroom. Label them with their names and where in the environment they were found, such as under a stone or growing on a tree.

Ideas for extension

Ask the children to design a poster to help other children to understand that they must treat animals and plants in the local environment with care. Encourage the children to use pictures to represent their ideas and help them to write simple messages.

Linked ICT activities

Talk to the children about creating signs to look after their local environment, such as 'Please do not pick the wild flowers.' Using a word processing program, for example 'Talking Write Away', 'Textease' or something similar, set up a word bank containing words that will help the children to create the signs. Show them how to add a picture or a border to their sign and print the sign out. Ask them where in the local environment they think the sign should be placed. Some of these signs may be placed around the school.

Plants and animals around us

spider	beetle	worm
giraffe	woodlouse	snail
sparrow	blackbird	rabbit
frog	deer	polar bear
grass snake	fox	fish

Plants and animals around us

ivy	daisy	wheat
palm tree	apple tree	grass
lichen	cactus	banana tree
stinging nettle	dock leaves	buttercup
pond weed	oak tree	water lily

Plants and animals around us

Draw pictures of three plants and three animals that you see on the walk. Write their names if you know them.

Plants	Animals
Name:	Name:
Name:	Name:
Name:	Name:

Name _____

Plants and animals around us

What sort of place did you visit? Circle words in the word bank.

Word bank

quiet	noisy	busy	dark	bright	damp
grassy	woody	muddy	shady	dry	wet

What did you find there?
Draw one animal.

Draw one plant.

Draw one animal you would find living under a stone.

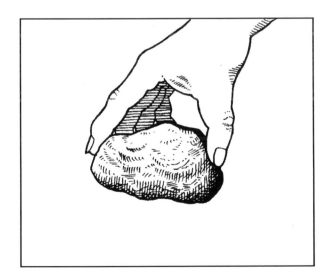

Draw one plant you would find living in the grass.

Name _____

Plants and animals around us

What sort of place did you visit? Circle words in the word bank
and add two more of your own.

Word bank

quiet   noisy   busy   bright   grassy   woody   muddy   shady

What did you find there?
Draw one animal.

Draw one plant.

Draw the place where you found
your animal.

Draw the place where you found
your plant.

Was it dry or damp there?

Was it sunny or shady there?

_____

_____

Name _____

Plants and animals around us

What sort of place did you visit? Write five words to describe it below.

What did you find there?
Draw one animal.

Draw one plant.

Draw the place where you found your animal.

Draw the place where you found your plant.

Why do you think it is living there?

Why do you think it is living there?

_____

_____

Habitats

A habitat is defined as the place in which an organism lives. Here it finds its food, spends most of its time, sleeps, reproduces and excretes its waste. Organisms can be found almost everywhere on Earth. The habitat of an organism includes not only the surrounding physical environment, but also the other organisms there.

In any landscape there will be many different habitats, with no distinct boundaries between them. Each habitat has its own specific set of conditions, such as levels of light, oxygen, humidity and temperature. The organisms found in any one habitat have features that have adapted to suit perfectly the conditions of that habitat. For example, aquatic plants, such as water buttercups, have large air spaces in their cells that allow them to float close to the surface of the water.

Within habitats are microhabitats where various species occupy different places within the same larger habitat. The variety of microhabitats in one larger habitat, such as the rainforest, is enormous. Even though scientists have studied such habitats for years, the exact number of species within a particular habitat is still very much unknown.

Types of habitat in the local environment

Here are some examples of the habitats that you may find in your local area, and the sorts of plants and animals that live there.

- Ponds contain still, fresh water and host a variety of plant and animal life such as lilies, Canadian pondweed, water boatmen, newts and frogs.

- Rivers are freshwater environments where the water is constantly moving downstream. The water may be slow moving or very fast moving. Many species inhabit rivers, such as trout and water buttercups.

- Canals and streams are freshwater environments where long stretches of water are often virtually motionless or move downstream very slowly.

Duckweed can be found in these habitats, and leeches may bury themselves in the muddy floor.

- Beaches are seaside environments that may be sandy or shingly, rocky or muddy. Many species living in this habitat bury themselves under the sand or shingle, such as limpets and crabs. Marram grass and sea holly can be spotted growing in the nearby sand dunes or rocks. Seaweed may be seen growing on the rocks.

- Estuaries contain a mix of salt and fresh water, so plants and animals living there are uniquely adapted to survive in either type of water. The movement of the tides presents further complications – twice daily not only the wetness of the area changes dramatically, but so too does the temperature. Examples of species in this habitat are flounder, sea trout and salmon.

- The sea is a mass of salt water that moves to and from the shoreline with the tide. A vast variety of organisms live in it, including sharks, jellyfish, sea anemones and plankton.

- Hedgerows are usually planted intentionally, to form a division between two areas of land. They provide a dark, sheltered environment for many species such as snails and slugs, violets and primroses.

- Grasslands tend to be open spaces where the main form of ground cover is grasses. Other plants, such as poppy and ox-eye daisy, grow alongside the grass plants. Animals – many of which are insects, such as ants and beetles – live within the grass and also underground, out of sight.

- Fields are usually maintained for farming. They can be grassy and used for animal pasture, or they can be planted with crops, such as cabbage and oil-seed rape.

- Woodlands are dominated by trees, making them a safe habitat for birds and small animals, such as hedgehogs and snails, and shade-loving plant species, such as bluebells.

- Forests are large areas of woodland covered by trees and undergrowth. They provide shady conditions for a wide variety of animals, such as deer, woodpeckers, grey squirrels and a variety of insects; and plants, such as oaks, wych-elms, foxgloves and bluebells.

- Buildings, whether made from wood, plastic, concrete or brick, provide homes to a variety of plants such as moss, lichens and ivy, which creep along the walls. Insects, such as spiders and woodlice, will find shelter in cracks and corners. Birds, such as starlings, nest in buildings.

- Waste sites harbour an amazing variety of animal and plant species, many of which are not visible to the naked eye – for example, disease-causing organisms like Salmonella and E. coli.

Protecting habitats

With more and more habitats being destroyed by human activity, such as clearing land, building and global warming, it is increasingly important to appreciate the diversity of species that are contained within the habitats that surround us. A tranquil woodland, although it may not be obvious to the naked eye, is seething with life. The soil is not only home to larger animals such as worms, woodlice and moles, but is riddled with insects, mites and fungi. Trees are home to birds, insects and squirrels and are also smothered in lichens, algae and moss. Within the microhabitat of the moss is found further life, and many animals found in woodlands may host parasites on their body surfaces.

Over the last 100 years there has been a significant reduction in the number of UK habitats. Habitats help to maintain the diversity of species, so it is very important to raise children's awareness of the need to maintain and restore habitats, so that the wildlife that lives there can continue to survive.

Visiting habitats

When visiting a local habitat, it is important for children to appreciate that the area they are walking through may be home to many different plants and animals. While looking for plants and animals that live in the habitat, they must take care not to disturb the environment. For example, if they turn over a stone or a log, they must replace it when they have finished looking. Also, remind the children to take care where they are putting their feet, because many animals and plants may be underfoot and will be damaged if stepped on. When looking for plants and animals, there is no need for the children to touch them or pick them up. They can look at them closely with a magnifying glass to see any details, but they will not learn a great deal more about them by touching them, and instead would probably harm the plant or animal.

When choosing two appropriate habitats for the visit, make sure there is a good amount of contrast between them (for example, light and shady, damp and dry).

All off-site visits must be carried out in accordance with your local authority and school guidelines. Make sure that all adults coming on the visit are as aware of the 'environmental care' rules as the children.

Habitats

Science objectives (Unit 2B)
- To know that there are differences between local habitats.
- To make predictions about the animals and plants found in different local habitats and to investigate these.
- To use drawings to present results and make comparisons, saying whether their predictions were supported.

Resources

- Generic sheets 1–3 (pages 64–66)
- Activity sheets 1–3 (pages 67–69), one copy for each habitat to be visited
- Clipboards
- Pencils
- Magnifying glasses
- Sticky-tack

Starting points: *whole class*

Introduce the term 'habitat'. Tell the children that all the different places they found on their walk in the last lesson and named on the chart are called habitats. Remind them about the different ones they found. 'We found a woody habitat and a shady habitat.'

Cut out and enlarge the pictures of habitats on Generic sheets 1 and 2.

Show them one by one to the children. Ask 'What sort of habitat is it?' and 'What can you see in the picture?'

As you are discussing the habitat and its features, ask the children to predict what sorts of plants and animals they might find there.

Use Generic sheet 3 to show examples of the sorts of plants and animals that can be found in the different habitats. The pictures could be cut out and shown to the children one at a time. They could stick each one to the picture of the habitat where they think they would find the plant or animal.

Once all the pictures of animals and plants have been sorted, invite the children to suggest other plants and animals that live in the habitats. Add the names of those plants and animals to the pictures as the children suggest them.

Ask the children if they think that they might see some of the animals if they visit this habitat. Discuss the fact that some animals will hide away from humans so we are not likely to see them, but we can often see signs that they have been there.

Tell the children that they are going to visit two different habitats to look at the plants and animals that live there. Describe each habitat in terms of those the children have seen in the Generic sheet pictures, highlighting the features of the habitats. Remind them of the plants and animals that they predicted would be found at each different place.

Before you leave for the visit, remind the children of the importance of not touching the plants and animals they see.

- If they turn over a stone or a piece of wood, they must put it back afterwards, because it is an animal's home.

- There is no need to pick up or touch any animals or plants – they are delicate and may be harmed or frightened by handling.

- They may use a magnifying glass to look at details.

- They should not touch the soil because it might contain microbes.

Group activities

Tell the children you are going to give them some activity sheets on which to record one plant and one animal that they saw on the visit.

Activity sheet 1

This sheet is aimed at children who need more support. They have to record in pictures the plants and animals they saw in the habitat. They have to choose features (from a list) that they saw in the habitat.

Activity sheet 2

This sheet is aimed at children who can work independently. They will be able to predict the plants and animals they find in the habitat. They have to draw and label the plants and animals that they find. Then they have to list features that they saw in the habitat (for example, mossy ground, tall grass, large stones). Display vocabulary banks to help them.

Activity sheet 3

This sheet is aimed at more able children. They have to predict and then record in pictures or writing plants and animals they saw in the habitats they visited. They also have to describe features of the habitat they visited and relate the features to the animals that live there.

Plenary session

Ask some of the children to report on the plants and animals they found. Were their predictions correct? Ask the children how the two habitats they visited were different. Record the differences in a chart on the board. Reinforce that different plants and animals live in different habitats because of differences in the environment. (Trees will not grow in an area where there is no soil. Fish will not live in an area where there is no water.)

Ideas for support

Provide a vocabulary bank for each of the habitats you have looked at.

Display the photocopiable 'habitats' word bank in the classroom (see page 147).

Use Generic sheets 1 and 2 to give the children the opportunity to practise matching plants and animals to the habitats they live in.

Ideas for extension

Ask the children to choose a question from:

- Where do spiders live?
- Why do birds live in trees?
- Why do frogs like damp places?
- Why do bluebells grow in woods?
- Does moss grow on trees?
- Where do snakes sleep?
- Why does ivy grow up trees?

This could be used in a whole-class question-and-answer session, or individuals could go away and research the answer and then present it to the class.

Linked ICT activities

Talk to the children about the different types of habitats. Ask them how they think they could find out more about the habitats and where they would look to find the information. They may suggest some books they have in school or at home. Talk about how they could find information using the internet. Ask them if they have ever used the internet. Show them how they can look for information. Enter the BBC website at www.bbc.co.uk

Let the children try looking at the website to find something they are interested in. Ask them to see if they can find out anything about plants and animals.

Habitats

Habitats

Habitats

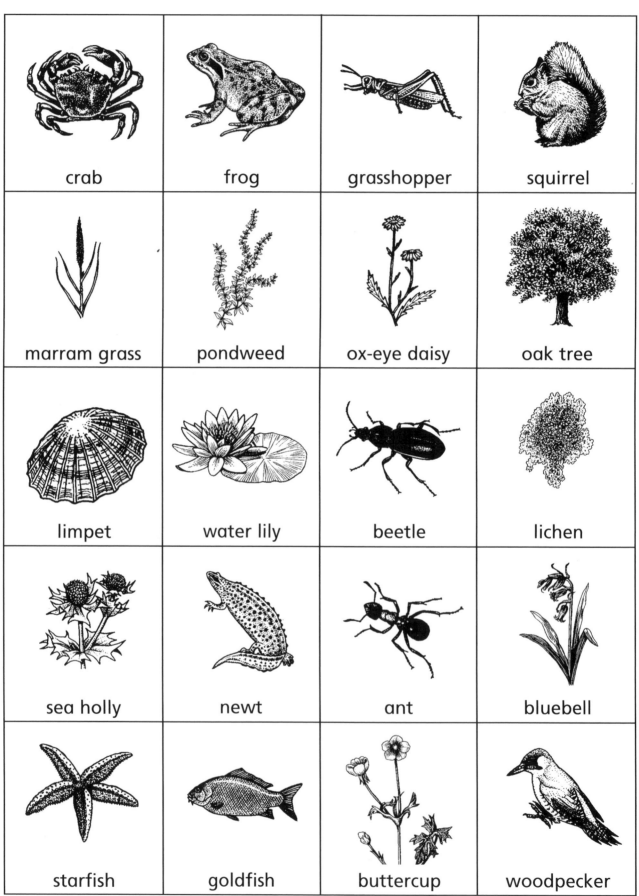

crab	frog	grasshopper	squirrel
marram grass	pondweed	ox-eye daisy	oak tree
limpet	water lily	beetle	lichen
sea holly	newt	ant	bluebell
starfish	goldfish	buttercup	woodpecker

Name _____

Habitats

I went to visit _____

I thought I would find _____ and _____

Draw plants and animals that you saw in this habitat.

What did you see in this habitat? Tick the boxes.

soil ☐   wood ☐   water ☐

trees ☐   stones ☐   bushes ☐

concrete ☐   grass ☐   sand ☐

Name ______________________________

Habitats

2
ACTIVITY SHEET

I went to visit ______________________________

I thought I would find ______________________________

____

Draw and label some plants and animals that you saw in this habitat.

On the back of this sheet, list the features of this habitat.

Name _____

Habitats

I went to visit _____

I thought I would find _____

_____

Draw or write about the plants and animals that you found in this habitat.

```


```

Complete these sentences.

This habitat was _____ and _____
When I looked around I could see _____ and

_____
The plants and animals I found live here because _____

_____

CHAPTER 8

Seeds of flowering plants

The life cycle of a flowering plant has evolved to ensure the continued survival of the species. Flowering plants have developed several different strategies that aid pollination, fertilisation and seed dispersal, using animals, the weather, or a self-built mechanism.

Flowering plant life cycles

The life cycle of a plant is often linked to the seasons of the year or to the life cycles of animals. Many plants reproduce in the summer when the Sun is high in the sky and the plant can trap the Sun's plentiful energy. Plants convert the Sun's energy to food, which provides the energy for flowers to grow. Insects are also more numerous in the summer, which helps flowering plants that need insects for pollination. In autumn, the plant produces seeds that are able to survive through the cold winter and then grow again in the warmer spring. In the winter, depending on the type of plant, the seeds lie dormant and survive the adverse conditions, although some die.

Flower and seed production

The flower is the reproductive part of the plant. First, pollination occurs when the pollen containing the male cells is put in contact with the female part of the plant, which contains the female cells. Fertilisation is the process where the male and female cells fuse to form a new cell. This new cell divides and increases in number inside a protective layer – this is now a seed. Seeds from different plants come in a huge variety of shapes and sizes.

Seed dispersal

Fruits are produced by a plant as a way of dispersing the seeds some distance away. If the seeds fell directly below the parent plant, then the area would become overcrowded and the plants would not grow properly. Fruits that carry seeds can look very different and this is related to the way that the seeds are dispersed.

Wind

Sycamores produce dry, flat fruits that can be dispersed by the wind. The large, lobed surface area easily catches the wind and as the light fruit falls, it spirals away from the tree. Wind also helps dandelion seed dispersal – the feathery tufts that hold the seed are easily blown kilometres away when there is a significant gust of wind.

Water dispersal

Seeds of plants that live in or around water may be carried from one place to another by the flow of the water. This dispersal will be particularly successful for seeds that float.

Consumption

Plants such as strawberries disperse their seeds by enclosing them in a juicy, sweet flesh. Animals eat them and the seeds (after travelling through the digestive system unharmed) are deposited in a different location with a plentiful supply of fertiliser. Other examples of such fruits are blackberries and holly berries. Plants that produce fruits to be consumed, develop the seeds ready for dispersal just as the fruits are ripe and ready to eat. This maximises the chances of successful dispersal and germination.

Carried on bodies

Burdock fruits are covered with tiny hooks that stick to the fur of animals and clothing people, to be carried far away from their original source. Other plants, such as goosegrass, have extremely sticky stems, leaves and fruits, which stick to clothes and animal fur as they are brushed past.

Self-built mechanisms

Pea plants produce seed pods that automatically split open when they dry, scattering the seeds a good distance from the parent plant. Poppy heads containing seeds sway in the wind and the poppy seeds fall out of small holes in the poppy head, a lot like salt falling from a saltcellar.

When the seeds fall, if the environmental conditions are favourable they germinate and grow into new plants, which then reproduce and generate more seeds. If conditions are unfavourable, seeds can lie dormant for many years until favourable conditions arise.

The length of a life cycle

The time it takes for one cycle to be completed varies greatly depending on the species. An annual plant does not live beyond a year – after producing flowers, seeds and fruit it dies. Examples of annual plants are marigolds, cornflowers and sunflowers.

A biennial plant takes two years to complete its life cycle. In its first year its primary role is to store food, while in the second year the food is used to produce flowers, fruit and seeds. Then it dies. Examples of biennial plants are hollyhocks, foxgloves and carrots.

A plant that grows year after year is known as a perennial. Although the part of the plant above the ground may lie dormant in the winter months, it will survive underground to grow again when the warmer weather returns. Examples of perennials are trees and fuchsias.

LESSON PLAN

Seeds of flowering plants

Science objectives (Unit 2B)
• To know that flowering plants produce seeds.

Resources

- Generic sheets 1 and 2 (pages 74 and 75)
- Activity sheets 1–3 (pages 76–78)
- Potted plant, seedlings and seeds of the same species of a flowering plant, such as tomato
- Selection of fruits such as apple, strawberry, sunflower, cucumber and sycamore
- Knife and chopping board
- Signs (enough for one per child) – 'adult plant', 'flowers', 'fruits', 'seeds' and 'young shoots'

Starting points: *whole class*

Show the children the potted flowering plant and the seedling of the same plant. Ask them if they know where the young seedling came from. Explain that just as humans and other animals produce young, so do plants and that the small seedling is the offspring of the plant. Show them a seed from the same species and help them to understand that this is what was planted in the ground (or compost) and has grown into a seedling.

Ask the children if they know where the seed came from. Reinforce that the flowers on a plant form seeds that are then planted (or fall) into the ground, then germinate and grow into small plants. The plants grow larger until they are adult plants, which then flower and the cycle continues. Cut out the pictures of the sycamore life cycle on Generic sheet 1. Ask the children which order they think the pictures should go in. Make the cycle on the board in a circular shape to emphasise that the cycle is ongoing. Label the stages 'seed', 'young seedling', 'adult plant', 'flower' and 'fruit'.

Generic sheet 2 can be used to show the children the seeds of a variety of plants. Also show them fruits of some plants where the seeds are visible (in an apple, on a strawberry) and also show them some examples of seeds that are visible in the flower head (on a sunflower).

Group activities

Tell the children that they are going to look for seeds in fruits.

Activity sheet 1
This sheet is aimed at children who need more support. They have to complete the pictures by drawing the seeds in place. It is useful for the children to be shown examples of the fruits, but they are likely to have seen them before as they are either edible or found in many local environments.

Activity sheet 2
This sheet is aimed at children who can work independently. They have to add the seeds to pictures of various fruits and label them according to the plants they come from. Then they have to draw two fruits of their own and label the seeds.

Activity sheet 3
This sheet is aimed at more able children. They have to add seeds to pictures of fruit. On the back of the sheet, they have to draw their own fruit, drawing in the seeds and labelling them. They also have to indicate how they think the seed will get to the ground, by choosing from a list.

Plenary session

Take the children into the hall or playground and split them into groups of five. Using the signs 'adult plant', 'flowers', 'fruits', 'seeds' and 'young shoots', mix them up thoroughly and give each member of the groups a sign to hold. Ask the children to move around randomly and then, when you give a signal, see if they can get into different groups of five so that each part of the life cycle is represented in the group. Once a group has all five stages, the children have to see if they can stand in a circle in the correct order of the life cycle. Before they begin to move about again they could swap signs.

Ideas for support

Cut up the cards from Generic sheet 2 (see page 75) and see if the children can match them correctly.

Make word banks associated with plant life cycles and display them in the classroom.

As an ongoing activity, grow a sunflower in the classroom through the year so that the children can watch it grow from a seed into a plant which then produces its own seeds.

Ideas for extension

Ask the children to draw a life cycle diagram of another plant, with labels. They could use reference books to help them.

Ask the children to find as many different ways as they can in which seeds are dispersed; wind, water, animals and so on. They will need access to reference books and CD-Roms to help them. Ask them to write up and illustrate their findings.

Linked ICT activities

Take in some packets of different seeds to show the children the differences in size. Talk to the children about the information on the seed packet and say that this is to tell you how to plant the seeds and when and where to plant them. Ask the children why they think there is a picture on the seed packet.

Tell them that they are going to make their own seed packet. Using a graphics program, such as 'Granada Colours', 'Fresco', 'Dazzle' or something similar, show the children how to use the paintbrush and fill tool to draw their flower. Show them how to use the text tool to add text and the name of their flower to the picture. Print out the picture and encourage the children to write some information on the reverse side of the picture.

Seeds of flowering plants

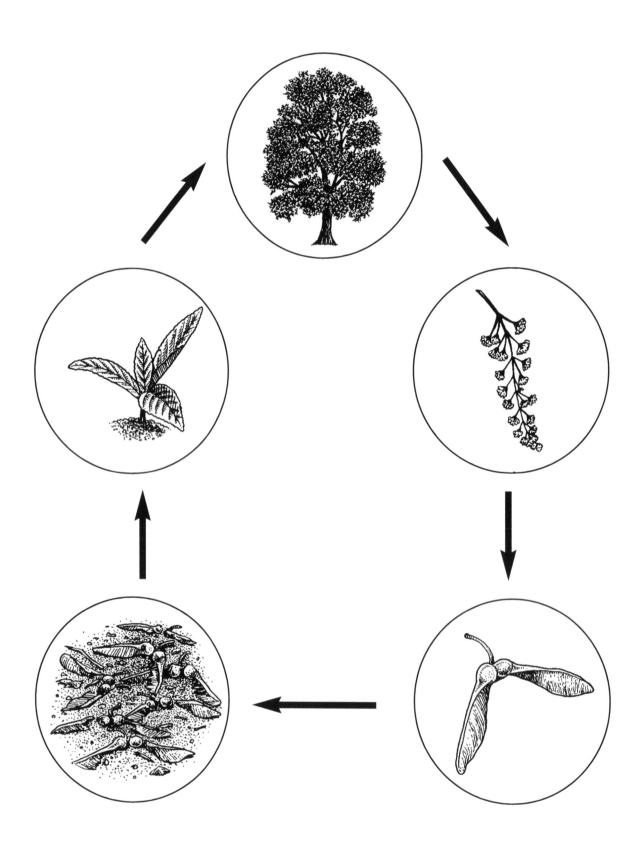

Seeds of flowering plants

Seeds of flowering plants

Draw where you think you would find the seeds in these fruits.
Label the seeds.

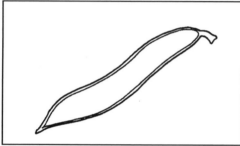

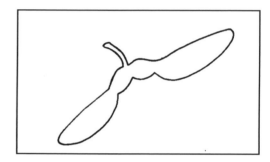

Which plants do the fruits and seeds above come from? Label them.
Use the word bank to help you.

Word bank

strawberry plant   sycamore tree   bean plant   cherry tree

Now draw the fruits of an apple and a cucumber. Draw them cut open so
we can see the seeds. Label the seeds.

Name _____

Seeds of flowering plants

Draw where you think you would find the seeds in these fruits.
Label the seeds.

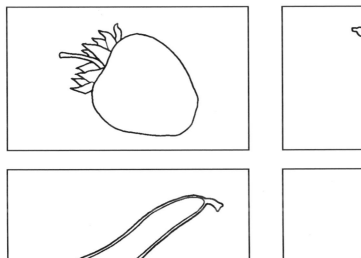

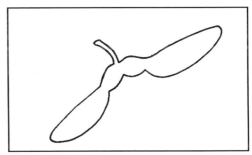

Complete the word bank below and use it to help you label the pictures to show which plants the seeds come from.

> **Word bank**
>
> _____berry plant   sycamore _____   bean _____   _____ tree

Now draw two fruits you know that have seeds. Draw them so we can see the seeds. Label the seeds.

Name —————————————————————————

Seeds of flowering plants

Draw where you think you would find the seeds in these fruits.
Label the seeds. Which plants do the fruits and seeds come from?
Label them.

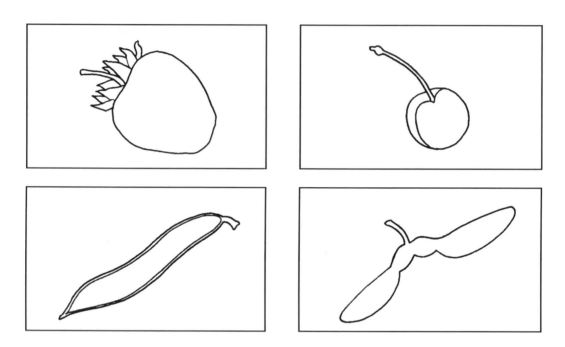

On the back of this sheet, draw the fruits of two other plants. Draw them cut open so we can see the seeds. Label the seeds.

On each drawing write a number to show whether you think the seeds will reach the ground by:

1. being eaten and passed out

2. being blown by the wind

3. sticking to the fur of animals

4. being thrown out by the plant.

Growing seeds

CHAPTER 9

TEACHERS' NOTES

From an early age, many children will be familiar with the concept of planting a seed and watching it grow, but they may not actually realise that seeds will only grow under certain conditions. If the conditions are not favourable, there will be no growth or the resulting plant will be unhealthy.

The formation of seeds

When a plant is fertilised, the ovary containing the ovule becomes the fruit, while the ovule itself becomes the seed. The pollen and the ovule join during fertilisation to form an embryo. The embryo is dormant until germination takes place. It can remain dormant for a long time – until conditions are right. The shape of the fruit that forms around the seeds depends on how the seeds will be dispersed. Seeds that are dispersed by animals have fleshy, juicy fruits surrounding them, to entice the animal to eat the seeds, or they have sticky or prickly outer surfaces to catch on animals' fur. Seeds that are dispersed by wind often develop around them a light structure with a large surface area, such as the winged fruit of the sycamore tree.

The structure of seeds

Seeds vary in shape and size but their internal structure is similar. Inside the seed, surrounding the embryo, are one or two leaves (cotyledons) which store carbohydrates and proteins to provide the energy and building blocks for growth after germination. The coat of the seed (testa) is very tough, which ensures that the contents of the seed are protected during dispersal and dormancy.

Triggering the growth of a seed

When a seed falls or is planted in a place where conditions are favourable, it first has to germinate. The process of germination begins when water is absorbed into the dry seed, causing the seed to swell and its outside coat to tear. Inside the seed is a store of nutrients that are now used as energy (before the plant can start making its own through photosynthesis). The nutrients are digested by enzymes (proteins that speed up chemical reactions) and carried to the embryo. The dormant embryo inside the seed begins to grow again.

Differences

Different seeds germinate in slightly different ways. In sweet corn, for example, first the embryo grows a root (radicle). Then a shoot breaks out of the top of the seed. A tubular sheath (coleoptile) protects the shoot and it pushes up through the soil until it breaks through the surface. Once above ground, the shoot continues to grow up through the coleoptile and develops leaves, which can then produce food for the plant by photosynthesis.

In other plants such as beans, the root of the embryo grows down, but the seed itself is pushed up out of the soil. From this, leaves develop and the seed (now that its nutrients have been used) shrivels and drops off, leaving the seedling. Examples of seeds that germinate in this way are oil-seed rape, mustard and cress.

In the pea plant, germination is different again. The seed remains in the ground and the shoot forms a hook shape to protect it as it pushes up through the soil. Once it has broken through, the hook straightens up and leaves grow at the tip of the shoot.

When germinating seeds in the classroom you should be able to distinguish which type of germination is taking place by looking closely at the shoot when it first emerges from the soil. Choose seeds that germinate and grow quite quickly under favourable conditions, so that the children do not become impatient waiting to see something happen. Seeds that grow quite rapidly are cress, sunflower and marrow. Sow the seeds into some good quality soil, keep them in a warm place and water them regularly. Germinated seedlings can be very fragile so must be treated with care.

Maintaining the growth of seeds

Once the shoot of the plant has reached the sunlight it continues to grow, using the supply of energy provided by the photosynthesising leaves. The plant cells multiply and grow in size. As the shoot and root grow, they are exposed to more sunlight and moisture in the soil and therefore grow more. As the plant continues to grow, some of its cells take on a specific role, such as carrying water, providing support or making and storing products the plant makes.

Growing seeds

LESSON PLAN

Resources

- Generic sheet 1 (page 83)
- Activity sheets 1–3 (pages 84–86)
- Fast-growing seeds, such as cress, sunflower, marrow or broad bean
- Water and a small watering can
- Soil, potting compost, sand and kitchen paper
- Pots and plates
- A magnifying glass

Starting points: *whole class*

Show the children some seeds and ask them what they would need to add for the seeds to begin to grow. From their previous work, they may already be aware that the plants will need water and light in order to grow healthily. Discuss whether or not plants need soil. They may have only seen plants growing in soil.

Tell the children that they are going to find out what seeds need to begin growing.

With the children, plan an investigation that will show what must be added to the seeds for them to begin to grow. Ask them to predict what they might need. Prompt them to suggest what they can try to grow the seeds in, to see whether plants do need soil to grow.

Help the children to set up an experiment. They should put seeds in a variety of places to see if they will grow, such as:

- in a pot of soil with water
- in a pot of soil with no water
- on a piece of wet kitchen paper
- on a piece of dry kitchen paper
- on a plate with no added materials
- on a plate with dry sand
- on a plate with wet sand
- in any other conditions the children might suggest.

Ensure that the children wash their hands after handling soil.

Ask the children to suggest what will happen to the seed as it begins to grow. Generic sheet 1 has pictures of a seed's stages of growth. Show the children each of the growth stages, one at a time. Emphasise that the part of the plant that grows up above the soil is the shoot, while the root is the part that will grow down into the ground.

Ask the children to look at the plants each day, and record what is happening to them. The children should record their predictions and findings in the form of a chart.

Conditions	I think that…	Day 1	Day 2
In dry soil			
In wet soil			
On wet kitchen paper			
On dry kitchen paper			
On a plate			
On a plate with dry sand			
On a plate with wet sand			

Ask the children if they think that seeds will grow in just water with no soil or other medium around them. Place some seeds in a small transparent pot with some water. Observe what happens daily and use a magnifying glass to look closely at what is happening.

Group activities

Tell the children that they are going to use pictures and sentences to show how seeds grow.

Activity sheet 1

This sheet is aimed at children who need more support. They have to sequence four pictures of a growing plant by numbering them (the first is done for them). They then have to complete three sentences (using a word bank) to say what seeds need to enable them to grow.

Activity sheet 2

This sheet is aimed at children who can work independently. They have to draw a missing picture in a series showing a seed growing into a plant. They then have to complete three sentences where the first letter of the missing word is given to them.

Activity sheet 3

This sheet is aimed at more able children. They have to draw two missing pictures in a series of pictures showing a seed growing into a plant. They then have to complete four sentences (without clues).

Plenary session

Discuss and compare the drawings the children have made of their seeds as they germinated and compare them with the pictures on Generic sheet 1. Some of the seedlings could be gently removed from their growing medium so that the children can look at the roots that will have grown. Discuss the direction in which the roots are growing.

Compare the results of the growing mediums. which medium gave the best results? Did the results differ greatly when the mediums were wet? Use the results to draw a conclusion about what plants need to grow. Compare this conclusion with the children's predictions. Did they predict correctly?

At the end of the investigation their results should conclude that seeds need water to grow but will grow in other mediums apart from soil.

Ideas for support

Use the pictures of the developing seed from Generic sheet 1. Shuffle the pictures in one set and then see if the children can put them in order of their growth.

If the school has a digital camera, take photographs of the growing seeds. They could be printed and laminated for the children to sequence them or to describe what is happening in the photographs.

Display the photocopiable 'plants' word bank in the classroom (see page 145).

Ideas for extension

Ask the children to look at reference books to find any evidence that supports their conclusions. For example, they will see pictures of plants growing in sand; can they find any pictures of plants growing on plates or without any water?

Ask some children to repeat the experiment with a different type of seed. Do they get the same results?

Linked ICT activities

Using pictures from this chapter, show the children how to sequence the pictures in a zigzag book. Using a word processing program such as 'Talking Write Away', 'Textease' or something similar, create a word bank of useful words for the children to use. Ask the children to create a sentence for each of the pictures to describe what is happening at the different stages of the plant growing. Add the sentences to the zigzag book. If there are any digital images of the plant growing add these to the book to create a class book on the growth of the seed.

Growing seeds

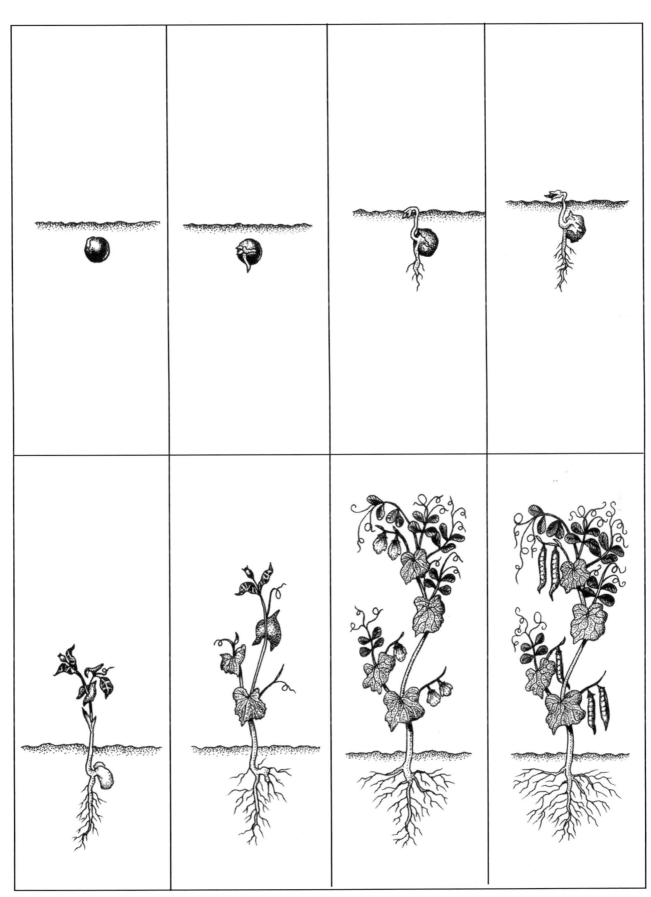

Growing seeds

Which order do the pictures go in? Number the boxes 1 to 4.
The first one has been done for you.

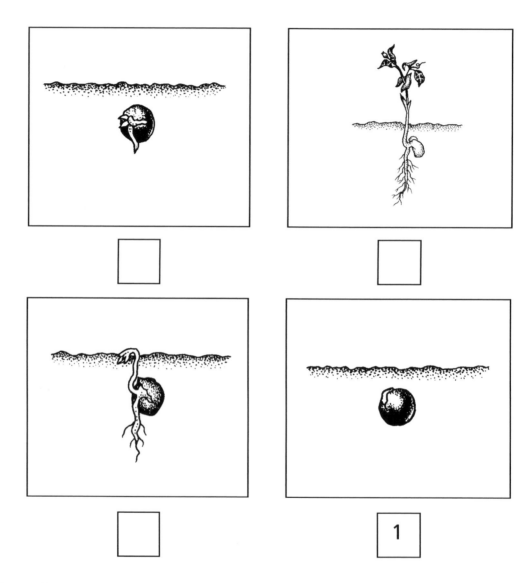

Complete the sentences. Use the word bank to help you.

Word bank

sand   water   soil

I found out that seeds need _____ to grow.

With water, seeds will grow in _____

With water, seeds will grow in _____

Name _____

Growing seeds

Draw the missing picture in the empty box to complete the sequence of growth from seed to seedling.

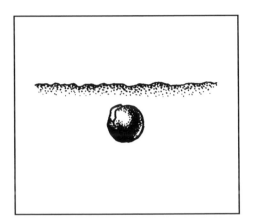
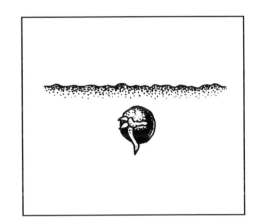

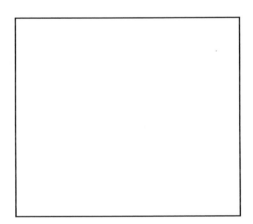
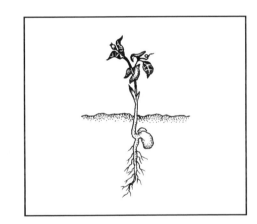

Complete these sentences.

We found out that seeds need w_____ to grow.

With water, seeds will grow in s_____

With water, seeds will grow in s_____

Name _____

Growing seeds

Draw the missing pictures in the empty boxes to complete the sequence of growth from seed to seedling.

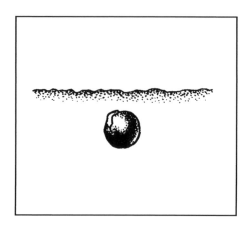

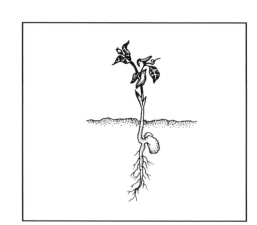

Complete these sentences.

We found out that seeds need _____ to grow.

With water, seeds will grow in _____

With water, seeds will grow in _____

With water, seeds will grow on _____

Life cycles

CHAPTER 10

TEACHERS' NOTES

A life cycle describes the series of changes in the life span of a living organism, including reproduction. The survival of a species depends on a continuation of this life cycle and its adaptation to the habitat in which it lives. Human intervention and destruction of habitats have led to the extinction of certain species (for example, the dodo, moa and passenger pigeon were exterminated by over-hunting).

In some life cycles the young look like miniature versions of their parents; for example, mammals and birds. Some other animals have a more complex life cycle where the young go through several distinct stages before they begin to look like their parents; for example, amphibians and insects.

Offspring that look like their parents

Mammals (including humans)

In every life cycle there are distinct processes and stages. With mammals, the mother gives birth to young that are very similar in characteristics to the parents. Although human babies look very different from older people, they share many characteristics, such as hair, arms, legs, body shape, teeth and facial features. The transfer of two sets of genes to a new organism ensures that no baby looks exactly the same as its parents and contributes greatly to variation within the species. As human babies grow, they pass through recognisable stages of childhood, adolescence and adulthood. As they continue to get older, they display specific characteristics such as grey hair, wrinkles and hair loss. Children will recognise a human baby, young child or adolescent straight away as being human, but they may not be able to so readily identify the young of an animal that looks nothing like its parents. (Note that monotremes are egg-laying mammals, such as the duck-billed platypus, and marsupials are mammals with a pouch, such as the kangaroo.)

Birds

Part of a bird's life cycle involves laying an egg. Once laid, the eggs are incubated by the parents to keep them warm. After a certain time period (which varies between species) the eggs hatch and the young emerge. The young birds are usually looked after by both parents, who protect and feed

them until they are ready to fly the nest. An exception to this is the behaviour of the cuckoo, which chooses the nest of a species that lays similar-looking eggs to its own. Unsuspecting parents incubate the egg, which then often hatches before the rest of the clutch of eggs. The cuckoo chick will push the other eggs or chicks out of the nest to ensure its survival as the only chick. (This behaviour enables the cuckoo to have many more offspring each season than it would be able to in its own single nest.)

Like humans, young birds look very much like their parents and share many of the same characteristics, such as a beak, clawed feet and feathered wings.

Offspring that do not look like their parents

Amphibians – frogs

The term 'amphibian' means 'two lives', which refers to the metamorphic life cycle of many frogs and toads where part of their lives is spent in water and part on land. The transformation that occurs between an immature form and an adult is known as a 'metamorphosis'. The life cycle of a frog starts with the fertilisation of the egg under water. The eggs are covered with a sticky, jelly-like substance, which dries out in the air. Hundreds of eggs are fertilised at the same time and the cluster of eggs is known as frog spawn. The larval form that hatches from the eggs (the tadpole) is herbivorous – in many ways it resembles a fish, having a fish-like tail and internal gills. During its metamorphosis into an adult frog, the tadpole slowly absorbs its tail and gills and grows four legs, and develops air-breathing lungs and a digestive system capable of digesting animal protein. This dual lifestyle is not true for all species of amphibians. Some species are entirely aquatic and others terrestrial. Some species, like the salamander, have larval young that are just smaller versions of the adult.

Insects – butterflies

Butterflies have a life cycle with four distinct stages. After an adult female butterfly mates and reproduces, she lays her fertilised white eggs on a specific plant, and will then leave them. After five days the eggs hatch into tiny larvae or caterpillars. They have proper legs to walk with, and a few additional prolegs that have suckers, helping them to cling to plants. They use their biting jaws to digest a tremendous amount of food and become much larger in size. The caterpillars breathe through small holes in their sides (spiracles). The body may be covered with bristle-like hairs (setae) to ward off predators. As the caterpillar grows in size it sheds its skin (ecdysis). After this has happened a number of times, the chrysalis (pupa) is revealed. The chrysalis then attaches itself to a branch or twig (some will just attach themselves by a silken thread, others will spin a cocoon first). The outer surface skin becomes a harder shell, which changes colour to camouflage it from predators.

Inside the chrysalis, changes are taking place to transform the caterpillar into a butterfly. The caterpillar inside is broken down and restructured to form a butterfly. After two to three weeks the adult butterfly will be fully formed, when the chrysalis begins to become more translucent, revealing the colour of the butterfly's wings.

When the butterfly is ready to emerge, the skin of the chrysalis splits and the butterfly crawls out. It will have six legs, a proboscis (that it uses to feed on liquids) and compound eyes (eyes consisting of many visual units). When it first emerges the wings are compact and the butterfly is limp. Blood is pumped into the wings to enlarge them and after a short rest, the butterfly is ready to fly. Adult butterflies only live for a short time so they quickly mate, reproduce and lay eggs and the process begins again.

The length of a life cycle

Human babies will, on average, spend more than 20 years growing and maturing before they reproduce. The life cycle of a Chinook salmon spans over five years. In contrast the life cycle of a butterfly is very short, with often only four months passing between the time the first and second batches of eggs are laid. The mayfly has an unusual life cycle – the adult mayfly lives for just three days but spends two years in its immature form.

Animals' longest-known life spans★

Adult mayfly	3 days
Mouse	3 years
Guppy	5 years
Swallow	9 years
Large beetles	10 years
Coyote	15 years
Giant spider	20 years
Toad	36 years
Lobster	50 years
Crocodile	60 years
Sea anemone	70 years
Elephant	77 years
Blue whale	80 years
Golden eagle	80 years
Sturgeon	100 years
Human	113 years
Tortoise	150 years

(★reproduced courtesy of John Stringer)

Life cycles

Science objective (Unit 2B)
• To know that animals reproduce and change as they grow older.

Resources

- Generic sheets 1–4 (pages 91–94)
- Activity sheets 1–3 (pages 95–97)
- Baby and adult photographs of yourself or another adult
- Plain paper, scissors and glue

Starting points: *whole class*

Show the children a photo of yourself when you were a baby, and then a more recent photo. Discuss how you have changed since you were a baby. Using Generic sheet 1, show the children a picture of a baby animal and then a picture of the corresponding adult animal. Prompt them to see that although changes occur, many of the characteristics will remain the same (arms, legs, body shape, facial features).

Tell the children that they are going to look at the life cycles of some animals. (A life cycle is the process of birth, growth, reproduction, ageing and death.)

Show the children Generic sheet 2. Talk about each stage of the life cycle of a bird. Ask the children how it is similar to the human life cycle (the young have characteristics of the adult) and how it is different (the young develop in eggs outside the mother's body).

Show the children the picture of the tadpole from Generic sheet 3. Ask them to predict what the tadpole may look like in a few years' time. If the children suggest one of the distinct life stages, introduce the corresponding picture to the class, pointing out the distinguishing features. If the children are not aware that the tadpole will change significantly in its first few weeks of life, reveal the fact that a tadpole will change in a different way as it gets older. Introduce the pictures of the life cycle in the correct order, explaining the changes that they can see. Position the pictures on the board

in a circle to show that the cycle is ongoing. Ask the children to help you label the different stages.

Introduce the children to the life cycle of a butterfly using Generic sheet 4. Talk to them about each stage of the life cycle.

Group activities

Tell the children that they are going to use the pictures and labels on their sheet to produce their own butterfly life cycle.

Activity sheet 1
This sheet is aimed at children who need more support. They have to cut out the four pictures of the butterfly's life cycle and sequence them to show the cycle. They have to label the pictures using a word bank (some words are needed twice).

Activity sheet 2
This sheet is aimed at children who can work independently. They have to cut out the four pictures of the butterfly's life cycle and sequence them to show the cycle. They have to label the pictures, and are given the first letters as clues.

Activity sheet 3
This sheet is aimed at more able children. They have to decide which part of the butterfly's life cycle is missing and draw it in. Then they have to sequence the pictures in the correct order and label the parts of the pictures.

Plenary session

Play a life cycle matching game using Generic sheet 1 (see page 91). Place all the pictures provided on a board face down. Invite the children to come out and choose two of the pictures. If they are part of the same life cycle then they make a pair. Challenge the children to match all the pairs on the board.

Ask questions such as:

- How many different stages does a butterfly go through?
- How many different stages does a human go through? Is there anything between baby and adult? What?
- What is a frog called in its youngest stage?
- Which animal can live for up to 150 years?
- Which animal only lives for three days?
- Name one animal that lays eggs.
- Name an animal whose young look like the adult.

Ideas for support

Help the children to relate the pictures on the activity sheets to those on Generic sheet 4.

Make word banks associated with the life cycles and display them in the classroom.

Photocopy the cards from the matching pairs game (Generic sheet 1) and let the children play the game in small groups.

Make an interactive display for the classroom with pictures showing the various stages in life cycles together with their corresponding labels. Each morning for a week, put up a different heading, such as 'The life cycle of a frog'. When the children come into the classroom in the morning, ask one of them to help you arrange the relevant pictures and labels on the board to display the life cycle.

Ideas for extension

Ask the children to use books to find any other animals that have a life cycle with more than one stage. Ask them to display their findings in a labelled life cycle diagram.

Ask the children to see if they can find out how long each stage in a life cycle lasts.

Ask the children to find out what the longest-living animal is (see the chart on page 88).

Linked ICT activities

Using a graphics program, such as 'Granada Colours', 'Fresco', 'Dazzle' or something similar, show the children how to use the symmetry tool.

Look at a variety of butterfly pictures and talk to the children about the patterns on the wings and how they are identical on each wing. Show them how the symmetry tool creates the same effect in the paint program. Draw a butterfly template for the children to complete by adding patterns, shape and colour to the wings. Let them experiment by changing the colours on the butterfly and the background to see the different results. Print out the pictures and add them to a wall display on life cycles.

Life cycles

Life cycles

The life cycle of a bird

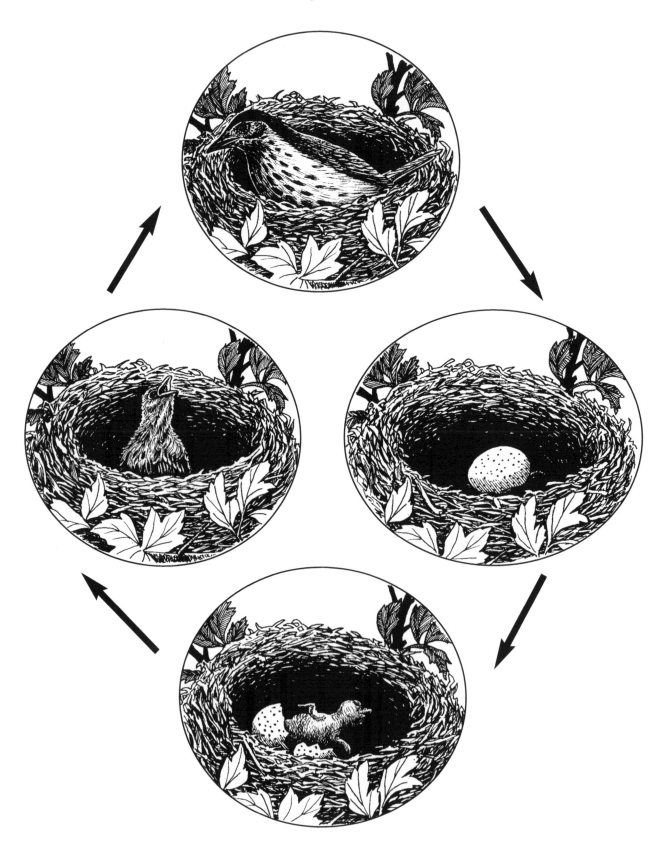

Life cycles

The life cycle of a frog

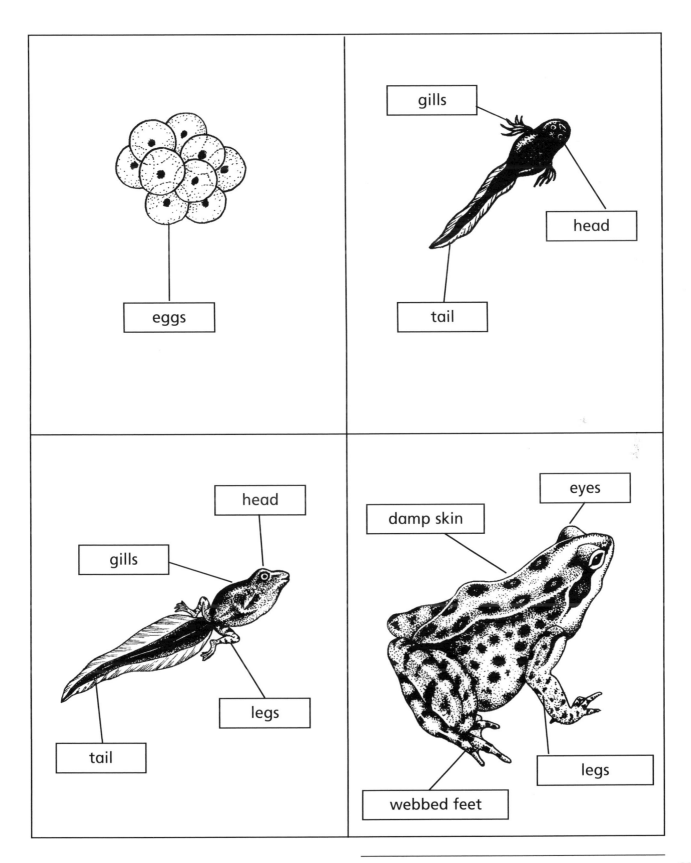

Life cycles

The life cycle of a butterfly

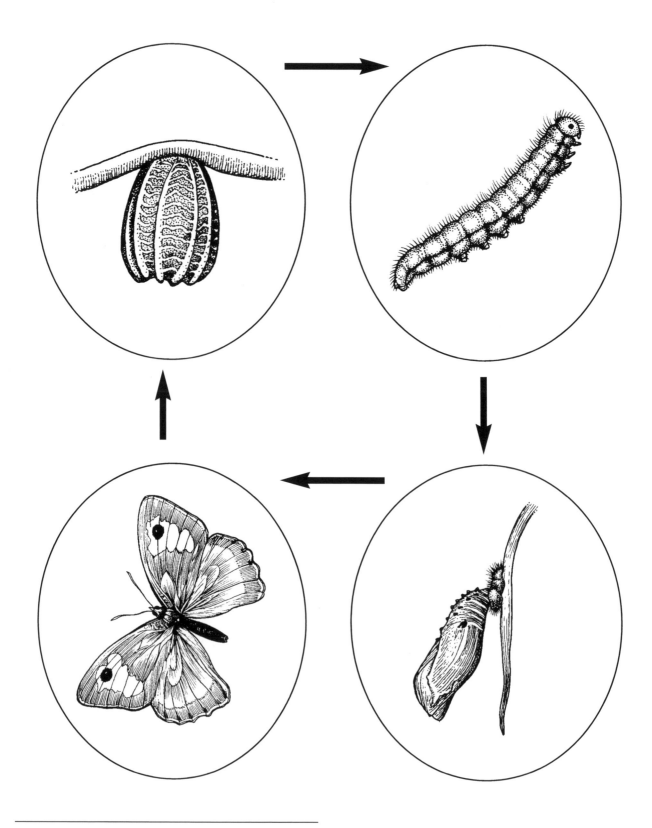

Name _____

Life cycles

Label the pictures below. Use the word bank to help you.

> **Word bank**
>
> legs   hard   shell
>
> sticky   wings   head   body   eyes

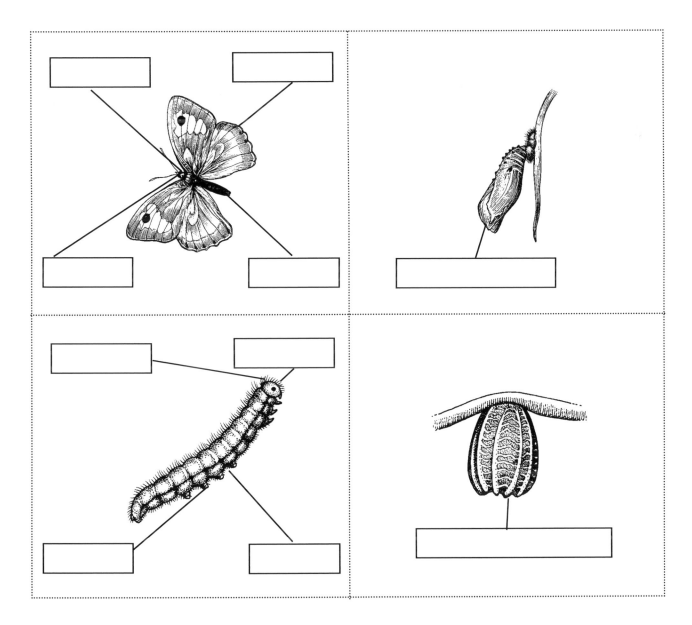

Then cut out the pictures and stick them on another sheet of paper in the correct order for the butterfly's life cycle.

Life cycles

Complete the labels on the pictures below.

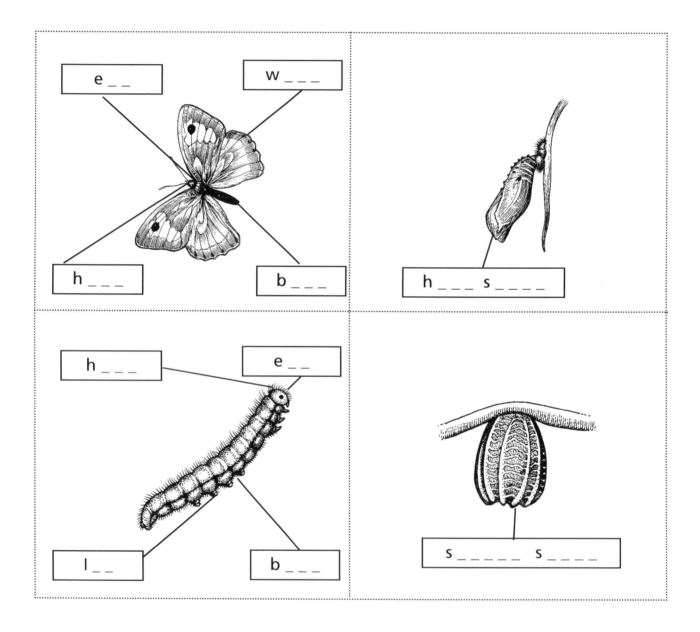

e _ _

w _ _ _

h _ _ _

b _ _ _

h _ _ _ s _ _ _ _

h _ _ _

e _ _

l _ _

b _ _ _

s _ _ _ _ _ s _ _ _ _

Then cut out the pictures and stick them on another sheet of paper in the correct order for the butterfly's life cycle.

Name _____

Life cycles

One stage of the life cycle below is missing. Draw it in the space and then label your picture.

Next, label as many parts of the other pictures as you can.

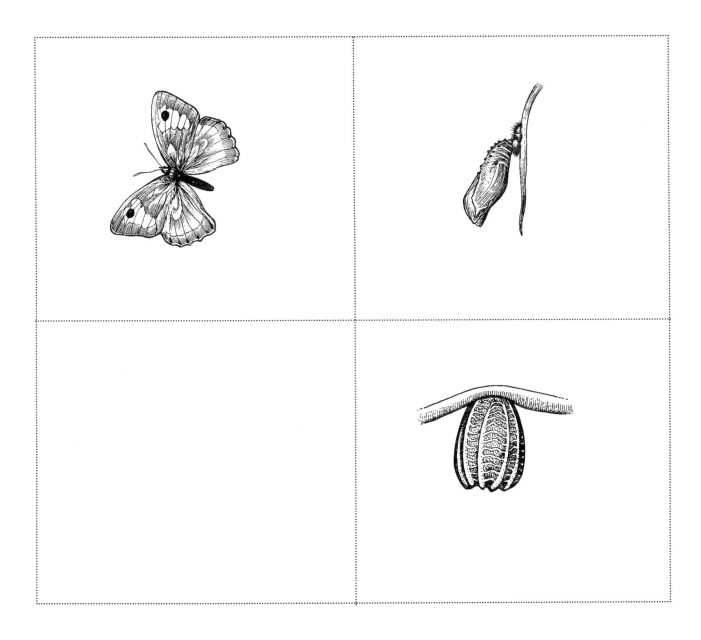

Cut out the pictures and stick them on another sheet of paper in the correct order for the life cycle of the butterfly.

Recognising characteristics

All living things share a number of common characteristics.

- They are able to grow.
- They can excrete waste products.
- They can reproduce.
- They respond to stimuli.
- They can respire.
- They need food and water to survive.
- They contain a complex substance called protoplasm.

Animals

Animals breathe in oxygen (from their surroundings), which is then absorbed into their bloodstream. Nearly all land-living vertebrate animals (those with a backbone) take in oxygen through their lungs, but some land-living animals, such as insects, absorb oxygen through specialised tubes (spiracles) set into their outer skeleton. Animals that live in an aquatic environment, such as fish, insect larvae and Crustacea, breathe using gills, which absorb oxygen directly from the water.

Animals all need to take water into their bodies, usually by drinking. Lack of water leads to dehydration and ill health. It is recommended that a human drinks eight glasses of water a day. Some animals, such as camels, live in arid places without access to large quantities of water. These animals have developed ways of living without a regular supply of water and can survive for fairly long periods without it.

Food also plays an essential part in the life of an animal. An animal's diet will vary considerably depending on the species, but all animals need to eat to generate the energy they need. Some animals are herbivores, eating only plants, while others are carnivores, eating meat. Some animals eat both plants and meat and are known as omnivores.

All animals can move in some way, but some are more mobile than others. The movement enables them to search for food, take shelter, find a mate and avoid predators. Some animals are fixed in one place (sessile) – such as the sea anemone, which is fixed to a surface but has moving tentacles which can capture food. The range of movement we see in animals varies from running, hopping and flying to swimming, slithering and gliding.

All animals reproduce and this can take place once or many times in a year, depending on the species. Sexual reproduction usually occurs when a male and female of a species mate. The gestation period (the length of time between conception and birth) varies in different species – humans carry young in their wombs for nine months, while rodents carry young for 21 days.

The young of some animals develop from an egg that is stored outside the female's body. These oviparous animals include birds, turtles, frogs and snakes.

Physical characteristics of animals

Children will often recognise animals because of their physical appearance. Animals' bodies may be covered with skin, hair, fur, scales or the harder substance chitin, which forms the outer bodies of insects such as woodlice, crabs and earwigs. They usually have legs or other appendages that enable them to move, such as wings or fins, and many have a tail. The head of an animal is often equipped with two eyes, a nose and a mouth and may have ears or other facial features such as cheeks and a forehead. Humans may have additional features such as freckles and eyebrows, while most animals have teeth or a beak.

Treating animals with care

Because animals have similar characteristics to humans, they can suffer from hunger, thirst, cold and pain just as we can. It is important for children to realise that animals need many of the things that we do, such as food, shelter and water, and that they should treat animals as they would want to be treated. If animals are kept as pets, then it is the owner's responsibility to ensure that they have what they need to live a healthy life. Animals that live in the local environment will find their own water, food and shelter, but we should make sure that we do not remove any of these things or disturb the animals unnecessarily.

Plants

It is much more difficult to observe many of the characteristics of plants. Children may not fully understand that a plant respires, moves and reacts to stimuli, because they cannot see these things happening. When animals breathe, their body moves as their lungs inflate and deflate, absorbing oxygen. It is much less obvious how this is achieved in plants. Oxygen is taken in by a plant through tiny holes in the leaves (stomata). Oxygen is also readily available in the plant's cells as a by-product of photosynthesis. At night when photosynthesis stops, plant respiration increases and the plant cells take oxygen from the outside atmosphere through the stomata.

Plants need water to grow healthily. Some plants need a large amount of water to fulfil their requirements whilst others can survive on a very small amount of water. Plants rely on water to carry out a number of essential processes. Water is taken up into the plants via the roots through the process of transpiration. As water is continuously lost to the atmosphere through evaporation via stomata in the leaves, a pull is created and fresh water is drawn up through the roots. Water is needed in the process of photosynthesis and also plays an important part in plant cell growth.

Plants need food to grow healthily, but most plants do not actually eat like animals. The few exceptions are species such as the Venus fly trap, which is carnivorous and catches insects by trapping them inside its leaves before dissolving them with a chemical and then absorbing them into its cells. Green plants make their own food by photosynthesis. In the presence of light, carbon dioxide and water, plants will produce oxygen and carbohydrates, which the plant can then use as a food source. Minerals and nutrients are also taken into the plant along with water through the root system.

Although plants are not able to get up and move towards sources of water and food, they can (very slowly) move and orientate their leaves and stems. Plants will often turn their leaves and stems in the direction of the Sun in order to maximise the amount of sunlight they can absorb. This response is called 'phototropism'. Roots show a response to stimuli called 'gravitropism', where the roots will always grow down regardless of which way up the seed is planted. Although these are reactions to stimuli, a plant is unable to react to a fire or flood in the way that animals do.

Physical characteristics of plants

Children will usually recognise a plant because of the presence of green leaves and a stem. Seed-bearing plants produce flowers, although children may not recognise them as such because not all flowers have brightly coloured petals. Roots are also a common physical characteristic, but these are usually hidden underground.

Recognising characteristics

Science objectives (Unit 2B)
- To observe and recognise some simple characteristics of animals and plants.
- To know that the group of living things called animals includes humans.
- To treat animals with care.

Resources

- Whiteboard with markers
- Sticky-tack
- Generic sheets 1–3 (pages 102–104)
- Activity sheets 1–3 (pages 105–107)
- An OHP

Starting points: *whole class*

Write two headings, 'plants' and 'animals', on the whiteboard. Cut out the characteristics on Generic sheet 1 and one by one read and show them to the children. Ask them to say whether these characteristics belong to a plant or an animal. Stick each characteristic under the appropriate heading. Discuss how some characteristics such as 'can move', have young', 'needs food' and 'can grow' will belong to both.

Use the headings 'plants' and 'animals' that are on the board. Cut out the pictures of plants and animals on Generic sheets 2 and 3 and show them to the children one at a time on an OHP. Ask the children whether they think that it is a plant or an animal and invite them to come up and stick it under the correct heading. Encourage them to tell you why they have chosen to put the pictures into a particular group. If they are not sure, remind them of the characteristics that you discussed earlier and ask questions such as:

- Does it have leaves?
- Does it have eyes?
- Is it covered with fur?

Ask the children if they know the specific names of the plants and animals.

When looking at the pictures of humans, ask the children if they know a different name used to describe people. Explain that our group of living things is called humans, and that although we are different from other animals, we are still animals.

Group activities

Tell the children that they are now going to sort living things into plants and animals.

Activity sheet 1

This sheet is aimed at children who need more support. They will be able to recognise whether a living thing is a plant or an animal. They have to tick the correct box to indicate whether the picture shows a plant or an animal and then colour the pictures.

Activity sheet 2

This sheet is aimed at children who can work independently. They have to record whether they think a living thing is a plant or an animal and also give a simple reason for their decision. On the back of the sheet, they have to draw another plant and another animal and write a sentence about each.

Activity sheet 3

This sheet is aimed at more able children. They have to sort plants from animals, then list some of the characteristics each group shows.

Plenary session

Play a game with the children, such as 'Name an animal with two legs', 'Name a plant with no flowers', 'Name someone in the class who has freckles', 'Name a plant with a red fruit', 'Name a tree that loses its leaves in autumn' and 'Name a teacher who has blonde hair'.

Discuss with the children how we should treat animals. Encourage them to see that animals are similar in characteristics to us and that animals need many of the things that we do – for example, food, shelter and water. Explain that we should treat animals as we would want to be treated.

Ideas for support

If the children find it difficult to distinguish plants from animals, ask them to look for clues on the board, where pictures and characteristics are grouped.

Make a word bank for the classroom to display related vocabulary in two groups, such as eyes, nose, animal; plant, stem, leaf.

Ideas for extension

Ask the children to look again at the list of characteristics that plants and animals possess from the list on Generic sheet 1. Ask them to list characteristics that apply to the following animals and plants: fish, giraffe, oak tree and bluebell.

Linked ICT activities

Collect pictures of fruits and animals the children will recognise. From a selection of five pictures of fruits, talk to them about the properties of the different fruits. Do they have skin? Can you eat the skin? Do they have seeds?

Using a simple branching database, such as 'Granada Branch', use the five pictures of the fruits and enter the questions you have asked into the branching database. Once the information has been entered the children will be able to use it to answer simple questions.

Recognising characteristics

fur	skin
can move	eyes
teeth	legs
nose	can grow
leaf	have young
petal	flower
stem	root
needs food	head

Recognising characteristics

Recognising characteristics

Name _____

Recognising characteristics

Does each picture show a plant or an animal? Tick the correct box.
Colour all the pictures.

plant ☐ animal ☐	plant ☐ animal ☐
plant ☐ animal ☐	plant ☐ animal ☐
plant ☐ animal ☐	plant ☐ animal ☐
plant ☐ animal ☐	plant ☐ animal ☐

Name _____

Recognising characteristics

Write 'plant' or 'animal' below each picture. Complete the sentence to say how you know this.

_____	_____
It has _____	It can _____
_____	_____
He can _____	It has _____
_____	_____
It has got _____	She has _____

On the back of this sheet, draw another plant and another animal.
Write a sentence about each, starting 'It has...' or 'It can...'

Name _____

Recognising characteristics

Sort these living things into two groups.

| dandelion | baby girl | caterpillar | fish |
| pondweed | chimpanzee | tree | |

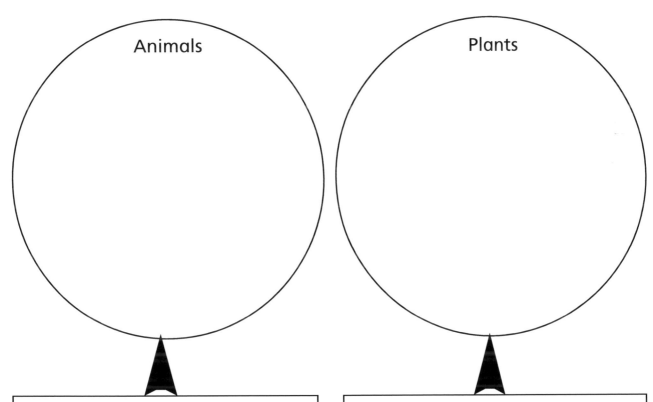

Animals

Plants

How do you know these living things are all animals?

How do you know these living things are all plants?

Similarities: humans and animals

Humans share many different features and many of these features are also shared with other animals. Many animal features have evolved over millions of years and have ensured survival. For example, mammals developed fur and became warm-blooded to be able to survive in cold climates. Humans are part of the animal kingdom, but we have features that make us more like each other than like other animals.

Why humans are similar

Looking at any number of humans, you will recognise many common features. We have two arms, legs and feet, hands with opposable thumbs (thumbs that enable us to grip), eyes, ears, a nose and a mouth. We have hair on our heads and our bodies and we walk upright. It is the variation in these features that enables us to identify individuals, such as different colour eyes and hair, different skin colour and type, and the size and shape of features such as noses and limbs.

The variation is due to the differences in the DNA (deoxyribonucleic acid) in each individual. A gene is a sequence of DNA that is coded for a specific protein. These proteins determine specific physical traits such as height, body shape, colour of eyes, hair and skin. Chromosomes contain thousands of genes. Each human cell contains 22 pairs of chromosomes and two sex chromosomes.

The genetic make-up of an individual is passed on to them by their biological parents, one half from each parent during the process of fertilisation. This is possible because egg and sperm cells contain only half the number of chromosomes that a normal cell contains. Each pair of chromosomes contains two copies of each gene (one from each parent) and it is the combination of these genes that determines an individual's characteristics. However, it is important to realise that characteristics shared by both parents may not be passed on to the children because some genes are more dominant than others – for example, two blue-eyed parents may have a child with green eyes.

The animal kingdom

The animal kingdom is divided up into several different classes and the species that are in each class are organised according to their physical features and characteristics. Humans belong in the class called mammals and although we differ from the other animals in this class, we share many of their characteristics.

Mammals

Mammals are warm-blooded, which means that their body continuously undergoes processes to keep it at a certain temperature. To help maintain this constant body temperature all mammals are covered in fur or hair. Another unique characteristic of most mammals is that they give birth to live young. (The duck-billed platypus and the echidna are exceptions because they lay eggs.) To feed their young, mammals have mammary glands that produce milk.

Birds

Like mammals, birds are warm-blooded and one of the reasons for this is that they need a high metabolic rate to provide the energy to fly. Like mammals, birds need insulation to help to keep them warm – in birds this is provided by feathers. A number of parts of a bird's anatomy have been adapted to enhance flight – for example, birds are toothless to make the head lighter for flying. A beak helps them to grasp and forage for food.

Reptiles

Unlike mammals, reptiles such as crocodiles and lizards are cold-blooded, which means their body temperature is the same as the temperature around them. They have no hair but are covered with a waterproof skin of scales instead. They are similar to mammals in that they have eyes and other facial features and teeth although these differ in number, shape and size. Some reptiles also have legs.

Amphibians

Frogs and toads are amphibians and these too are cold-blooded. They have many of the same facial features as mammals and also have legs that they use to hop or walk. Some amphibians differ in that their young do not resemble the adult and have very different characteristics. The eggs of a frog first develop into tadpoles, which have no legs and a tail. (A human baby has the same characteristics as an adult, but in a smaller form.)

Fish

Fish are cold-blooded animals and apart from their facial features (eyes, mouth) they are not similar to mammals. Their body is covered with scales and lacks limbs, having fins and a tail instead.

Invertebrates

All the above classes of animals have one thing in common with mammals – they have a backbone and an internal skeleton and are called vertebrates. The remaining classes of animals have much less in common with mammals – they lack a backbone and an internal skeleton and are consequently known as invertebrates. The group of animals classed as arthropods includes insects, spiders and crustaceans such as crabs and lobsters. They all have a hard external skeleton (exoskeleton) and their bodies are segmented. Like mammals they have a head and legs, but these are often in multiple pairs; they usually have eyes although there may be more than two. Phyla of animals that have even less in common with mammals are the annelids (an example of which is an earthworm), nematodes (which include hookworm), and molluscs (which include slugs and snails).

One thing that all these animals have in common with mammals is that they have all evolved their different characteristics to enable them to reproduce and adapt to an environment where they can obtain sufficient necessities, such as food and water, to survive.

Similarities: humans and animals

Science objectives (Unit 2C)
- To know that humans are more like each other than they are like other animals.
- To make careful observations to identify similarities.
- To know that humans are similar to each other in some ways and different in others.
- To explore human variation, making observations and comparisons.

Resources

- Whiteboard and sticky-tack
- Generic sheets 1 and 2 (pages 112 and 113)
- Activity sheets 1–3 (pages 114–116)
- An OHP
- An orange, a tngarine and a banana

Starting points: *whole class*

Show the children three pieces of fruit: an orange, a tangarine and a banana. Ask them if they can tell you which fruit are similar. Discuss why they are similar and what 'similar' means. Ask them to name two other fruits that are different. Discuss what 'different' means and how the fruits are different. Choose two children and discuss how they are different and similar. Discuss features that could be changed, such as the length and colour of hair, and those that can't, such as the presence of freckles.

Show the children the pictures on Generic sheets 1 and 2 using an OHP. Then organise them into small groups and give each group a set of the pictures to sort in any way they want. Ask each group to explain to the class how they have sorted them. Ask:

- Which animals are humans?
- How are all the humans similar?
- How are all the animals in that group similar?

Now choose two of the pictures, such as the cat and the camel. Show them to the children and ask them to tell you if they are similar or different (similar). Encourage them to give you reasons, such as they both have eyes or they both have fur. Choose other sets of two pictures leading to other comparisons, such as one has a tail but the other does not or one has fur but the other has scales.

Now show the children three pictures together – hold one in your hand and stick the other two to the whiteboard. Ask the children if one of the animals on the board is more similar to the animal you are holding. Again, prompt them to give you reasons for their answers, such as 'They both have legs, but this animal has two legs like the picture you are holding,' or 'They both have eyes, but one of them has the same shaped eyes as the picture you are holding.'

Group activities

Tell the children that they are now going to look for similarities and differences between animals. Remind them what the words 'similar' and 'different' mean.

Activity sheet 1

This sheet is aimed at children who need more support. They have to look at pairs of animals (including humans) and decide if they are similar or different. They have to show one way in which they are similar (or different) by circling one feature on each of the 'similar' and 'different' pictures.

Activity sheet 2

This sheet is aimed at children who can work independently. They have to choose animals that are similar to each other, recording their choice by linking the animal they think is most similar to the one in the middle of each set. They then have to draw two animals: one similar and one different to that shown on the sheet.

Activity sheet 3

This sheet is aimed at more able children. They have to say whether two animals are similar or different, writing two reasons for their answer. They are also asked to draw two animals that are different, given two reasons why they are different.

Plenary session

Choose three children of the same sex to stand up. Ask the other children for reasons why two of them might be more similar than the third. Encourage them to look at all the different features the children might have, such as colour of hair, height and freckles. Be sensitive to any children who may have birthmarks. Discuss skin colour differences with sensitivity. Ask the children to try and curl their tongues in from the sides. Some will be able to and others not; this is not something that can be learned – the ability is hereditary.

Ideas for support

Display the photocopiable 'animals' word bank in the classroom (see page 146).

Use the pictures from Generic sheets 1 and 2 to play a game in a small group. Share the cards out. The teacher or an adult helper could call out features, such as 'It has two eyes.' The children have to put down a card showing an animal with the feature. The winner is the child who puts all their cards down first.

Ideas for extension

Ask the children to make a fact file about two friends. They could draw a picture of each friend and then put down points about them, such as 'She has long hair and he has short hair.'

Linked ICT activities

Have a selection of familiar animal pictures available for the children to use. Ask them to select one of the pictures. Tell them they are going to describe five things about the animal on a tape recorder without saying the name of the animal. Use a tape recorder to record the children. Place all the animal pictures on the table and play back the tape recordings to see if the children can identify the animal from the descriptions given. Play this activity using just ten pictures at a time.

Similarities: humans and animals

Similarities: humans and animals

Name _____

Similarities: humans and animals

Look at the pairs of animals and tick the box to say if they are similar or different.

	Similar ☐ Different ☐	
	Similar ☐ Different ☐	
	Similar ☐ Different ☐	
	Similar ☐ Different ☐	

On each pair of 'similar' pictures, put a circle around one thing that is similar.

On each pair of 'different' pictures, put a circle around one thing that is different.

Name _____

Similarities: humans and animals

Look at the animal in the middle of each set. Which is similar: the animal on the left or the right? Link the similar animal to the one in the middle. Circle one thing that is similar.

 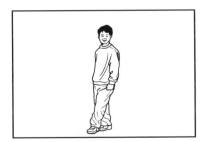 

 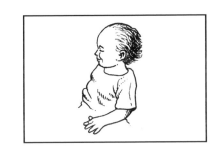 

Draw a similar animal here.   Draw a different animal here.

Similarities: humans and animals

Circle the correct answer, 'similar' or 'different', and give two reasons.

similar or **different**
-
-

similar or **different**
-
-

similar or **different**
-
-

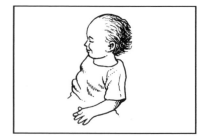

similar or **different**
-
-

similar or **different**
-
-

Draw two animals to match this.

similar or **different**
- One animal has scales and no legs.
- One animal has legs and hair.

Similarities and differences: plants

CHAPTER 13

TEACHERS' NOTES

As in the animal kingdom, there is a great deal of variation in the plant kingdom. The plant kingdom is also divided into many phyla and classes on the basis of similar characteristics. These are mainly concerned with similar physiology, such as the presence of a developed vascular system for water and mineral transport.

Fungi used to be classified as a group within the plant kingdom but they are now commonly excluded so that the plant kingdom now only contains green plants. Fungi (including mushrooms and toadstools) are not classed as plants because they do not contain chlorophyll and cannot make their own food. They obtain their food from dead or living things.

Vascular system

Plants are divided into those that have a vascular system and those that do not. Mosses and liverworts (a phylum called bryophytes) have no vascular system, so they have very little support, which means that they have very little height. The bryophytes have 'stems' and 'leaves' but they are very different in structure to flowering plants. They are green plants, capable of photosynthesis, and their stems and leaves have stomata which help the exchange of gases in the cells.

The phyla of plants with a developed vascular system are much more numerous, with great variation between the classes. There are two phyla with a developed vascular system: the pteridophytes (ferns, club mosses and horsetails) and the spermatophytes which are divided up into the gymnosperms (conifers) and the angiosperms (true flowering plants).

Angiosperms

Flowering vascular plants, or angiosperms, are further divided into two groups according to the structure of their seeds: monocotyledons and dicotyledons. Dicotyledons have two cotyledons (the seed leaves that are part of the embryo inside the seed), and monocotyledons have one cotyledon in the seed.

Monocotyledonous plants

Examples of monocotyledons are cereal crops – such as wheat, corn and rice – and grasses, lilies and orchids. The veins in their leaves are parallel and the leaves themselves are often blade-like. The vascular system is a complex pattern of bundles of xylem and phloem, which carry water and solutes around the plant. Many fine fibrous roots protrude from the base of the stem, their function being to anchor the plant and to absorb water and minerals from the surrounding soil. There is a great deal of variety in flower structure, ranging from the feathery structure found in grasses to the highly complex unique floral structures of orchids. The petals are often arranged in multiples of three.

Dicotyledonous plants

The majority of flowering plants are dicotyledonous, such as buttercup, daisy, oak and sycamore. Leaves come in a wide variety of shapes and sizes, from the lobed oak tree leaf and heart-shaped ivy leaf to the waxy, pointy holly leaf and the oval, serrated rose leaf. The leaves all share a net-like system of veins.

The vascular system is made up of xylem vessels and phloem cells, but they are arranged in a ring at the periphery of the stems, with the xylem being on the inside and the phloem on the outside.

The roots of dicotyledonous plants usually form a main tap root. In vegetables, such as carrot and parsnip, this acts as storage for carbohydrates and can be a source of food for humans and other animals. Smaller lateral roots branch out from this. These roots facilitate water uptake and also anchor the root firmly into the soil. The petals of dicotyledonous flowers are often arranged in multiples of four or five. Dicotyledonous plants such as broccoli, cabbage and oil-seed rape have a distinctive cross-shaped flower structure, defining them as 'crucifers'.

Similarities

Throughout the plant kingdom there are many variations in leaf shape, size and vascular structure. The leaves are green because they contain chloroplasts (containing the green pigment chlorophyll, responsible for trapping sunlight during the process of photosynthesis). One similarity in every plant species is that the leaf has evolved to be the major photosynthetic organ of the plant, and is therefore the major source of the plant's food. The leaves have stomata that help the exchange of gases and water. Floral structures throughout the plant kingdom vary greatly in colour, number of petals, size and shape, but their function is reproduction, regardless of whether the pollination (the transfer of the male pollen to the female part of a flower) comes about by wind, insects or self-pollinating mechanisms.

Similarities and differences: plants

LESSON PLAN

> **Science objectives (Unit 2C)**
> - To know that plants in the local environment are similar to each other in some ways and different in others.
> - To make observations and comparisons of local plants.

Resources

- Generic sheets 1–3 (pages 121–123)
- Activity sheets 1–3 (pages 124–126)
- A selection of potted plants, such as a spider plant, ivy and an umbrella plant
- Two plants with their (different) roots washed clean of soil
- Clipboards and pencils
- OHP
- For each child, a card with 'similar' on one side and 'different' on the other

Starting points: *whole class*

Show two potted plants at a time to the children and ask them to say how the plants are different. Encourage them to look at the leaves and any flowers, and also the stems, which may have buds on them or may be different colours or different shapes. Show two plants that have had the soil washed off their roots, so that they can see and compare the roots.

Show the children Generic sheet 1 enlarged on an OHP. Ask them if they can see any leaves that are similar in shape and any that are very different. Encourage them to describe the shape of the leaves and to look for any other features such as veins. Repeat this activity with Generic sheet 2, which shows different flowers. In particular, talk about the shape, size and number of petals. Explain to the children that some flowers will be exactly the same in shape and structure but will look different because they are a different colour.

Take the children for a walk in the local environment. Give them a copy of Generic sheet 3 on a clipboard and ask them to draw pictures of two plants they find that are similar to each other and two plants that are different. They could label the parts of the plants that they know. In the 'Other information' boxes they should record observations that they might not be able to show in the drawing, such as colour and detail on the leaves.

Group activities

Tell the children that they are now going to draw similar and different plants.

Activity sheet 1
This sheet is aimed at children who need more support. They should be able to recognise that plants have either similar or different leaves. A plant (snowdrop) has been drawn for them and its leaves described. They have to draw a plant that has similar leaves, and then a plant that has different leaves. They could label the leaves on the pictures they draw and colour the plants.

Activity sheet 2
This sheet is aimed at children who can work independently. They should be able to recognise similarities and differences in the flowers and leaves of plants. Given an example (daisy), they have to draw a plant that has similar leaves and flowers, then a plant that has different leaves and flowers. They have to describe the leaves and flowers they have drawn. They could label leaves and flowers on the pictures they draw and colour the plants.

Activity sheet 3
This sheet is aimed at more able children. They should be able to recognise similarities and differences in flowers, leaves and stems. Given an example (primrose), they have to draw a plant that has similar features and a plant that has very different features, and describe them. The children could label leaves, stems and flowers on the pictures they draw and colour the plants.

Plenary session

Make individual cards of the pictures of leaves and flowering plants on Generic sheets 1 and 2. Give to each child one of the cards with 'similar' written on one side and 'different' on the other. Hold up two of the picture cards of leaves (or flowers or plants) and ask the children to hold up their card to say whether they are similar or different. Holding up signs is quieter than the children calling out, and will help you to assess who can recognise similar and different plants.

Ideas for support

To reinforce understanding of 'similar' and 'different', take some photographs of plants found in the local environment and ask the children to point out similarities and differences they can see between them.

The children could collect leaves from local trees and trace round them or make leaf prints with paint. They could make a labelled display showing leaves that are similar and those that are different.

Make a word bank for the classroom to display related vocabulary such as leaf, leaves, stem, plant, buds and veins.

Ideas for extension

Bring some leaves into the classroom, mounted on card. Ask the children to find out the names of the plants that the leaves come from. Give them some cards to put the names of the plants on. They can use the cards to play matching pairs.

Give the children a photograph of a plant in their local environment and ask them to make a picture of it using collage materials. They will need to look carefully at the shape of the leaves and the detail they can see and should be encouraged to choose suitable materials for colour and texture.

Linked ICT activities

Use a digital camera to take photographs of plants that are found in your local environment around the school. Using a word processing program, such as 'Talking Write Away', 'Textease' or something similar, add a photograph of the plant to the page.

Set up a word bank with useful words and ask the children to write two sentences describing the plant in the photograph.

Similarities and differences: plants

oak leaf

snowdrop leaf

fern leaf

clover leaf

holly leaf

beech leaf

primrose leaf

pine leaf

thistle leaf

Similarities and differences: plants

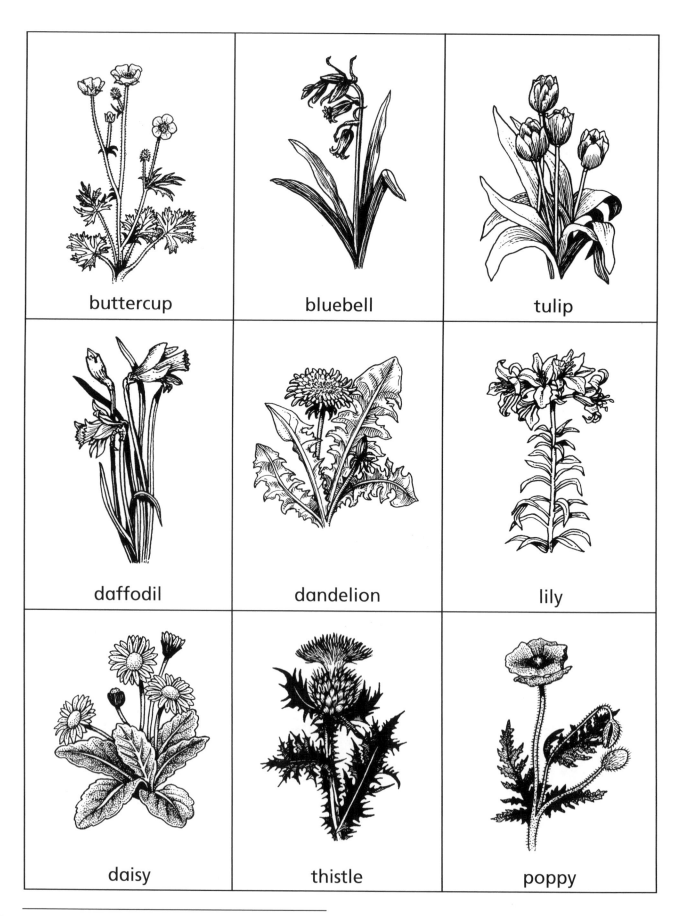

buttercup	bluebell	tulip
daffodil	dandelion	lily
daisy	thistle	poppy

Similarities and differences: plants

Look at the plants growing in your local environment.
Draw two plants that are similar.

Picture	Picture
Other information	Other information

Draw two plants that are different.

Picture	Picture
Other information	Other information

Name _____

Similarities and differences: plants

ACTIVITY SHEET

Look at this plant.

The leaves on this plant are long and thin.

Draw a plant that has similar leaves.

The leaves on this plant are

Draw a plant that has different leaves.

The leaves on this plant are

Name _____

Similarities and differences: plants

Look at this plant.

The leaves on this plant are wide and have a vein down the middle. The flowers on this plant have lots of small petals.

Draw a plant that has similar leaves and flowers.

The leaves on this plant are

The flowers on this plant are

Draw a plant that has different leaves and flowers.

The leaves on this plant are

The flowers on this plant are

Name _____

Similarities and differences: plants

This plant is a primrose. The stems are tube-shaped and hairy. There are five petals on the flower and they are all the same colour. The leaves are large with curly edges and they have a vein down the middle.

Draw a plant that is similar.

Draw a plant that is very different.

Describe this plant.

Describe this plant.

Measuring differences

CHAPTER 14

TEACHERS' NOTES

Animals or plants of the same species may bear the same characteristics but can often look different because of the size of their features. These differences can be measured and compared using standard units, such as centimetres, or non-standard units, such as Multilink or hands. When discussing differences with the class, remember that some children may be sensitive to their height or build and may not want parts of their bodies compared or measured.

Height

One of the most obvious comparisons children can make between themselves is their height. In a primary class you will probably find that you have a mixture of taller boys and girls, average boys and girls and shorter boys and girls. As the children get older, a pattern is likely to emerge where the boys begin to overtake the girls in most cases, and on average become taller as adults. Genes, inherited from our parents, can often have a significant effect on what we look like. If one or both parents are particularly short or tall, their children may be taller or shorter than average. This is not always the case and factors such as development in the womb may also affect the height of an individual. The tallest man ever to have lived was an American named Robert Wadlow who died in 1940. He measured 267.5cm (8ft 11in). The tallest person living in Britain in May 2003 was a Somalian, Hussain Bisad, who measured 232.5cm (7ft 9in). Some people are taller or shorter than average because of medical conditions. When measuring their height, the children can use height measuring apparatus designed for the job, or can just as easily place a book on their head and stand with their back to a flat wall or door and mark with sticky-tack where the book meets the wall. The distance from the floor to the mark on the wall can then be measured using centimetres or a chosen non-standard unit.

Head circumference

Newborn babies usually have their head circumference measured, and it is measured again at intervals during childhood. Measurements like these can be an indication that the head and brain are growing as they should be – they will grow at a certain rate in proportion to age. Children can compare the circumference of their heads by measuring them using a tape measure or a piece of string, which they mark and measure later with a ruler. Milliners measure the circumference of people's heads in order to be able to make a hat that fits perfectly.

Limbs

Human legs and arms come in all different shapes and sizes. Children can use a tape measure to measure the length of a leg. The measurement can be taken from the hip down to the sole of the foot. The concept of having an inside and outside leg measurement taken (as when being measured for a pair of trousers) can be discussed but it is easier if young children take the outside leg measurement. It would be useful for the children to compare the leg length of tall people because a tall person may not necessarily have long legs but may have a long torso.

Arms can be measured from the top of the shoulder to the wrist, or the arm and hand could be measured as one unit from the top of the shoulder to the tip of the middle finger. A tape measure would be the most suitable measuring apparatus for this. The arm span could also be measured using a ruler or tape measure from the tip of one of the middle fingers to the other with the arms horizontally outstretched. The children could also investigate whether or not there is any truth in the theory that our arm span should measure exactly the same as our height.

The length of hands can be measured from the wrist to the tip of the middle finger, or the length of the hand span can be measured (with fingers and thumb stretched as wide as they can). When children are measured to have shoes fitted, the shop assistant will measure the length and width of their feet to ensure that the shoes they wear are not restricting their feet, which could cause problems. One way to make it easier for young children to take measurements of their hands and feet is to draw round them and then measure the shapes on the paper. Some children will need help with this to get an accurate drawing and therefore accurate measurements.

Facial features

It is possible to measure the size of many facial features, such as nose, eyes, ears, mouth and lips, but these are small features in comparison with others and will be more difficult for younger children to measure accurately. Care must also be taken when holding measuring apparatus close to any facial feature, particularly the delicate eye area.

Torso

Measurements can also be taken of waists and chests, with tape measures or string. It is important to be sensitive to children who may be significantly over or underweight, avoiding use of terms such as 'skinny' or 'fat'. Tailors and designers who make clothes will regularly measure people's waists and chests.

Hair length

Hair length is a characteristic that can be measured in the classroom using a tape measure. Hair is different because its length can be controlled. People choose to have hair of a certain length but do not have any choice when it comes to the length of their arms, toes and noses (unless they resort to cosmetic surgery).

Humans usually begin to stop growing at the end of adolescence, but some people continue to grow for many years after this, for different reasons. Even when humans reach a much older age, body measurements are not likely to remain static because, in the very elderly, height, length of limbs and overall features shrink slightly.

Measuring differences

LESSON PLAN

Science objectives (Unit 2C)
- To know that some differences between themselves and other children can be measured.
- To measure hand span in standard units of length.
- To present measurements in block graphs.
- To make comparisons of hand span.
- To raise questions about differences between themselves, test them and decide whether their predictions were correct.

Resources

- Activity sheets 1–3 (pages 131–133)
- Rulers, tape measures and height stands
- Roll of wallpaper
- Pens

Starting points: *whole class*

Ask three children to stand in front of the class and discuss with everyone the differences between them, such as eye colour, freckles and height. Ask if it is possible to measure any of the differences and if they are unsure, ask 'Could we measure how tall the children are?' and 'Could we measure how blue the children's eyes are?'

Ask a child to lie on a strip of wallpaper on the floor so that you can draw round them. Record on the child's outline any differences the children think can be measured, by drawing round that particular part of the outline of the child's body or adding notes or arrows to the outline.

Introduce the idea of measuring cubits and explain what a cubit is (the straight-line distance between the elbow and the end of the longest finger). Ask some children to place one arm on the board for you to draw round, and use these to help them understand what to measure. Give the children tape measures and ask them to practise measuring their own and each other's cubits. Ask them to find out if the length of the cubit on their left arm is the same as their right. Ask them if the person sitting next to them has a longer or shorter cubit than theirs.

Make a tally chart of the measurements made. You could do this as a whole class, or the results could be collected in groups.

Introduce the idea of measuring hand spans and explain what a hand span is (the straight-line distance between the thumb and little finger when fingers and thumb are splayed). Ask some children to place a hand on the board for you to draw round. Use these to help them understand what to measure. Ask all the children to measure their hand span. Make a tally chart from the results.

Group activities

Tell the children that they are now going to make a bar chart about hand spans.

Activity sheet 1

This sheet is aimed at children who need more support. They have to answer questions about a bar chart that shows the measurements of some fictional children's hand spans. They then have to make their own bar chart to show the sizes of the hand spans of five children in their class.

Activity sheet 2

These children have been given some information about the hand spans of a group of fictional children and have to complete the bar chart to show this information. They then have to answer questions about the information in the bar chart. Finally, they have to make their own bar chart to show the sizes of the hand spans of ten children in their class.

Activity sheet 3

These children are required to make their own bar chart using the given information, so they need to have had practice in doing this before. They then answer the questions about the bar chart and finally make another bar chart showing information about all the children in their class.

Plenary session

Look at the results by showing one of the children's graphs. Ask:

- What is the smallest hand span in the class?
- What is the largest hand span?
- What size hand span do most children have?
- Do you think that the children with the biggest hand span will have the biggest feet?

Line the children up in order of their shoe size and see if the one who had the biggest hand span has the largest feet.

Ideas for support

The children may need help measuring in centimetres and so could use non-standard measures such as Unifix or Multilink instead.

Ideas for extension

Set the children the task of finding out if it is true that their arm span is the same length as their height. Help them to measure and record their measurements, and discuss whether they need to measure more than one person to test the theory out.

Ask the children to find out whether it is true that the length of their nose is the same as the length of their ears.

Linked ICT activities

Talk to the children about how we are the same and how we are different. Identify things that make us different, such as the colour of our eyes and hair.

Create a fact file with the children about themselves, recording their hair colour, eye colour, hand span and so on. Using a database program such as 'Pick a Picture' complete the datafile using the file 'Ourselves' from this program. Having entered their data, using the pictures provided in the program, work with the children to find answers to questions such as 'How many children have brown hair?' and 'How many children have blue eyes?' Print out the graph of the information and use the printout to ask questions, such as 'How many children have brown hair?' and 'How many have blue eyes?'

Measuring differences

This is a bar chart showing the sizes of some children's hand spans.

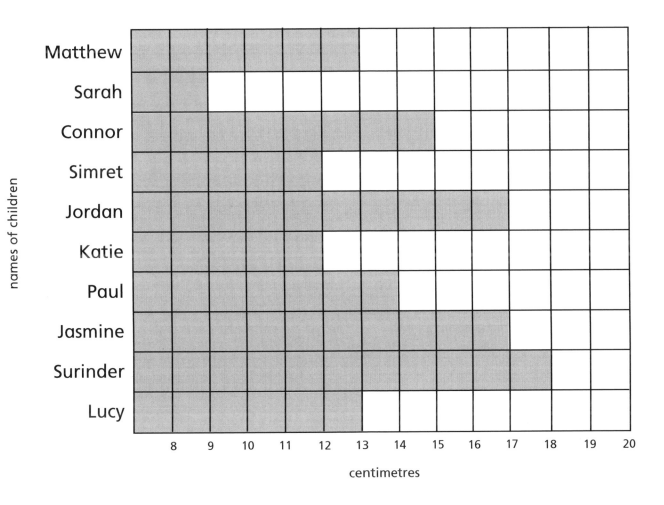

names of children

centimetres

Who has the longest hand span? _____

What size is it? _____ centimetres

Who has the shortest hand span? _____

What size is it? _____ centimetres

Which two children have 12cm hand spans? _____

What size is Lucy's hand span? _____ centimetres

Now make a bar chart to show the hand spans of five children in your class.

Name _____

Measuring differences

Use this information on hand spans to complete the bar chart.

Matthew: 13cm; Sarah: 9cm, Connor: 15cm; Simret: 12cm; Jordan: 17cm; Katie: 12cm; Paul 14cm; Jasmine: 17cm; Surinder: 18cm; Lucy: 13cm

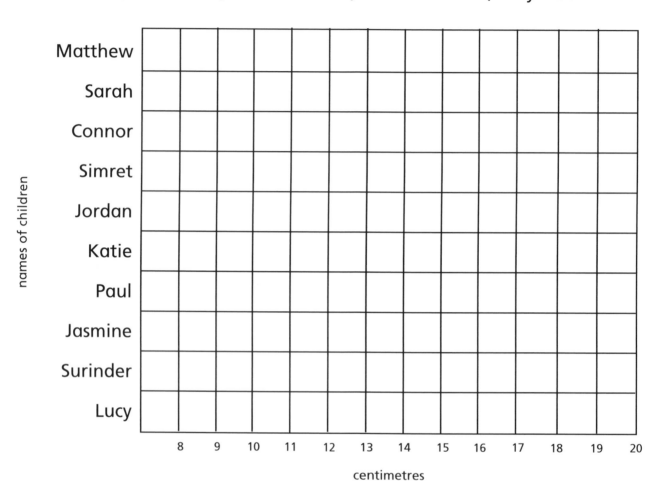

Who has the longest hand span? _____

What size is it? _____ centimetres

Who has the shortest hand span? _____

What size is it? _____ centimetres

Which two children have 12cm hand spans? _____

What size is Lucy's hand span? _____ centimetres

Now make a bar chart to show the hand spans of ten children in your class.

Name _____

Measuring differences

Use this information on hand spans to draw up a bar chart using the grid below.

Matthew: 13cm; Sarah: 9cm, Connor: 15cm; Simret: 12cm; Jordan: 17cm; Katie: 12cm; Paul 14cm; Jasmine: 17cm; Surinder: 18cm; Lucy: 13cm

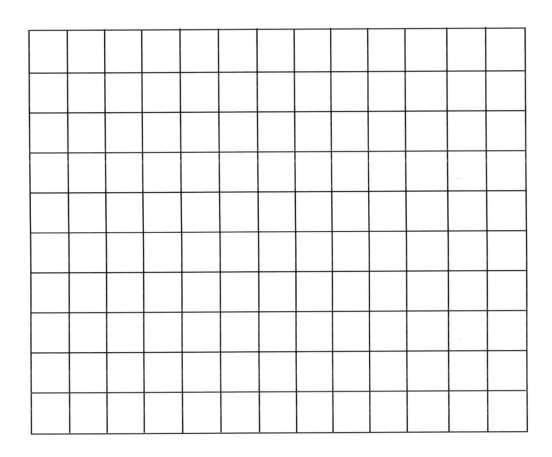

Who has the longest hand span? _____

What size is it? _____ centimetres

Who has the shortest hand span? _____

What size is it? _____ centimetres

Which two children have 12cm hand spans? _____

What size is Lucy's hand span? _____ centimetres

Now make a bar chart to show the hand spans of all the children in your class.

CHAPTER 15

Grouping living things

Plants and animals can be grouped according to their characteristics. Both the plant and animal kingdoms are divided into different phyla, and within these are further divisions again. This grouping allows us to distinguish between and learn more about species that have similar although not always observable characteristics. External distinguishing features can be identified and compared by observation.

Plants

When looking at similarities and differences between plants in the local environment, observations will be of the parts of the plants that can be seen above the ground and not of the internal or underground structure of the plant. Plants can share many similar features even though they can differ greatly in size from the mightiest oak tree to the smallest daisy.

Leaves

Variation in leaves provides a number of criteria for grouping plants. Leaves are different shapes, sizes and colours (shades of green), their veination and textures vary, and how they are arranged on the stem is different depending on the species. Some plants, such as mint, have leaves that are lined up in identical places on either side of a stem; others, such as the snapdragon, alternate. Other patterns of leaf growth include a spiral pattern around the stem, a whorl about the stem or a rosette of leaves at the base of the plant.

Flowers

Flowers can differ in many ways. The number of petals a flower possesses can vary greatly, as can the shape and colour of the petals. The organisation of the flowers on the stem will vary too. Some plants will bear a single flower while others will have many flowers arranged in clusters or groups.

Stems

Stems differ in the shape of their cross-section, with some being square and others round. One similar feature in any plant species is that stems bear leaves positioned in a way that is beneficial to the plant. Some stems are woody while others are not, and some are hairy or thorny or grow in a twisted fashion as opposed to straight up. The main role of a stem is support, and much of this comes from the woody xylem vessels that form long hollow tubes along the length of the stem.

Animals

Animals have many more features that are similar and different than plants do. Many of these are features that can be identified by observation. One of the most obvious features may be the animal's overall size. A horse will be much larger than a bee, but even animals of the same species may differ in size with much of the variation being related to their age.

Tail and limbs

Another obvious similarity or difference may be the number of limbs; animals such as the millipede have many legs, while worms have none. Tails are another feature that may or may not be present. Many animals in the local environment will have a tail, such as squirrels, birds, mice and rabbits. Some insects, such as the earwig, may have a more specialised apparatus such as a pair of pincers situated at their rear end. Feet are another part of an animal's anatomy that varies depending on the type of species: a pig will have trotters, while horses and sheep walk on hooves; birds and squirrels have claws and ducks have webbed feet. Each animal has feet that enable it to move around its habitat successfully.

Facial features

Facial features in animals are often similar – two eyes, a nose-type shape and a mouth. Some animals, such as mice, have ears while snakes do not. Even though a mouth is almost always present, the animal does not always have teeth – in birds, a beak replaces teeth, and slugs and snails do not have teeth either. A nose, in addition to being the major scent organ in many animals, is used to help breathe in oxygen and expel carbon dioxide. But in animals such as fish, this function is controlled by the gills on either side of the head. The eyes of animals vary in shape, size, number and also position. The eyes of fish are positioned on the side of the head as opposed to the front; snails have eyes that are mounted on stalks. Some animals, such as the earthworm, have eyes but they do not see very well – their eyes really only help them with light orientation. Spiders usually have eight eyes.

Body parts
The body structure of animals varies – mammals have a head, a trunk and limbs. The body of an insect is divided up into three parts – the head, thorax and abdomen (legs are attached to the thorax). Spiders' bodies are made up of a head and abdomen and are joined by a narrow waist. Worms are a group of animals with linear bodies that are arranged in segments.

Body cover
Skin, usually with an additional layer of scales, hair or fur, covers animals' bodies. Mammals are warm-blooded and so are covered with a layer of fur or hair to help maintain a constant body temperature. Other animals such as amphibians, reptiles and fish are cold-blooded. Many have scales that cover their skin and are adapted to their aquatic habitat, providing little water resistance and drying quickly out of water. Invertebrate animals (without a backbone), such as insects and crustaceans, have their skeleton on the outside of their body (an exoskeleton) made up of a substance called chitin, often looking as though they are wearing a suit of armour. Because chitin is such a hard and brittle substance, these animals have to shed or moult their exoskeleton when they grow.

Wings
Many species have wings, such as birds and most insects. Wings are always present in pairs. Birds' wings are made of feathers and skin while insects' wings are an extension of the exoskeleton that covers their thorax. Muscles attached from the body enable the wings to move up and down. Most birds and insects have the ability to fold their wings when resting.

Movement
Moving is another feature that can be used to group animals. Some animals are capable of many different types of manoeuvre – frogs can walk, hop and swim, and most birds can walk, hop and fly. Other animals are capable of only one type of movement – for example, snakes can only slither and slugs only slide.

Local environment

See the guidelines for walks on page 7.

When looking at features it may be useful to use a magnifying glass to look at small details, such as the veination on a leaf or the antenna on an insect. Young children may not be able to record accurately enough what they observe outside the classroom to enable them to sort the living things into groups when they return. A camera may be useful to make a permanent record of observations that were made of similarities and differences found in plants and animals in the local environment. Emphasise to the children that there is no reason to take plants and animals from the local environment into the classroom.

Grouping living things

Resources

- Generic sheets 1–4 (pages 138–141)
- Activity sheets 1–3 (pages 142–144)
- Clipboards and pencils
- Scissors and glue
- Chalk (to draw sorting circles on the ground) or hoops
- Cards with animals' names for each child

Starting points: *whole class*

Explain to the children that a graph is a way of showing quite a lot of information easily. One way a graph can present information is through the use of pictures. Show the children Generic sheet 1 – a graph of plants found in one local environment. You could introduce this graph through a story – a pen friend of yours who lives in another part of the country is a gardener. She has asked what sorts of plants you have in your local environment so you have had a look and then put your information in a graph so that she can see it easily. Explain to the children that the plants were sorted into these groups. Ask questions such as:

- How many of the plants have flowers?
- How many more flowers with five petals are there than flowers with one petal?

Put the children into small groups. Give each group one cut-out set of the animals from Generic sheets 2 and 3. Ask them to sort the animals into three groups using three sorting circles drawn in chalk (or give three hoops to each group). Make sure they complete the label on each sorting circle. When they have finished, ask them to explain to the class how they decided to group the animals. (They might all have chosen different criteria.)

Fieldwork

Take the children for a walk in the local environment and ask them to record any living animals that they see on their walk, by drawing and writing. Remind them that people are living animals so they can be included. If there are too few (or no) animals seen to be able to sort them into groups, then ask the children to brainstorm animals that they know live in the local environment from previous work (see Chapter 6).

Ask the children to think of different ways that they could group the animals. Remind them of some of the criteria they can use, such as humans/not humans, legs/no legs, tails/no tails.

Group activities

Tell the children that they are now going to group some animals and record them on a block graph.

Activity sheet 1

This sheet is aimed at children who need more support. They have to sort the animals by body covering, cut out the pictures and complete the block graph.

Activity sheet 2

This sheet is aimed at children who can work independently. They are given two groups they could use to sort the animals and have to think of three more. They have to cut out the pictures of animals and complete the block graph. They have to add one animal picture of their own to the graph.

Activity sheet 3

This sheet is aimed at more able children. They have to group the animals in any five ways they choose, labelling the block graph accordingly. (If necessary, prompt them to think about the animals' covering.) They have to cut out the pictures and complete the graph. They have to add two animal pictures of their own to the graph.

Plenary session

Take the children into the school hall or playground and give them each the name of an animal from Generic sheet 4 (see page 141). Draw three large circles on the floor in chalk. Write a label in each circle, such as 'I have feathers', 'I have a scaly skin' and 'I have hair or fur'. Explain the circles to the children and then ask them to stand in a circle where they think they belong. (Not all the animals fall into these groups.) Then change the labels on the circles to 'I can fly', 'I have no legs', 'I am an amphibian'. (Again, not all the animals fall into these groups.) Go on to talk about where one animal could fit into more than one group, such as 'I can fly' and 'I have feathers'.

Ideas for support

Play a game with Generic sheets 2 and 3, where the animals are sorted by an adult and the children have to guess how they have been grouped. (Have all the humans been grouped together? Have all the animals with tails been grouped together?)

Ideas for extension

Ask the children to make up some animal riddles using the animals' observable characteristics. For example:

I am not a human
I have four legs
I have hairy skin
I have two large ears
I have a very, very long nose
What am I?

Answer: an elephant.

Encourage them to use characteristics that are specific to a certain type of animal.

Answers to plenary games

I have feathers	I have scaly skin
Robin	Snake
Sparrow	Lizard
Blackbird	Tortoise
Duck	Crocodile
Swan	Turtle
Parrot	Goldfish
	Salmon

I have hair or fur	I can fly
Human	Robin
Rabbit	Sparrow
Dog	Blackbird
Mouse	Duck
Cow	Swan
Hamster	Bat
Bat	Bee
Mole	Wasp
Bee	Ladybird
Wasp	Butterfly
	Parrot

I have no legs	I am an amphibian
Snake	Frog
Worm	Toad
Snail	Newt
Goldfish	
Salmon	

Linked ICT activities

Organise the children into groups of four or five. Play the game 'What's in the box?' Give each group an empty box with a soft toy or a picture of an animal inside, taking care not to let each other know what animal is in the box. Using a word processing program, such as 'Talking Write Away', 'Textease' or something similar, ask the children to work in their groups to write some key words and sentences that will give clues as to what is in the box. Seal the boxes and put them on display on a table. Put a piece of paper next to each box and ask the children to write their guess on the paper next to the box. Leave the boxes for a week and open them at the end of the week to reveal the answers.

Grouping living things

A graph to show the plants found in our local environment

Number of kinds of plants

| 1 petal | 4 petals | 5 petals | 6 petals |

Number of petals on one flower

Grouping living things

d.

Grouping living things

Grouping living things

robin	salmon	wasp
sparrow	human	ladybird
blackbird	rabbit	butterfly
duck	dog	worm
swan	mouse	snail
lizard	hamster	frog
tortoise	cow	toad
crocodile	bat	newt
turtle	mole	parrot
goldfish	bee	snake

Grouping living things

Cut out the animals below. Stick them in the correct group on the block graph.

A graph to show the animals in our local environment

Number of animals

fur   scales   hard skin   feathers   soft skin

What the animals are covered in

Name _____

Grouping living things

Look at the two group labels on the graph. Think of three more groups and write them on the graph. Cut out the animals and stick them in the correct group. Draw one more animal of your own on the graph.

A graph to show the animals in our local environment

Number of animals

fur   soft skin

What the animals are covered in

Grouping living things

Choose five groups and sort the animals below into those groups.
Cut out the pictures and complete the block graph. Draw two
animals of your own on the block graph.

A graph to show the animals in our local environment

Number of animals

Photocopiable word banks

adult plant	grow	seedling
bark	healthy	shoot
branch	leaf	soil
bud	light	stem
dark	moss	tree
fern	petal	water
flower	plant	wilted
fruit	root	
grass	seed	

Photocopiable word banks

adult animal	feet	nose
arms	fish	reptile
baby	fur	scales
beak	gills	shell
bird	hair	skin
body	head	tail
child	human	teeth
claw	insect	webbed feet
eyes	legs	wings
feathers	mammal	

Photocopiable word banks

beach	fence	pebble	stone
branch	field	pond	stream
brick	grass	pool	sunny
bush	ground	river	tree
canal	hedge	rock	trunk
cliff	light	sand	underground
concrete	log	seaweed	wall
damp	moss	shade	water
dry	muddy	shady	wet
earth	nest	soil	wood

Useful resources

Resources recommended for linked ICT activities

Software

Counter for Windows Granada Learning/
BlackCat Software, Granada Television, Quay
Street, Manchester M60 9EA, Tel 0161 827 2927
www.granada-learning.com

My World series Granada Learning/SEMERC,
Granada Television, Quay Street, Manchester
M60 9EA, Tel 0161 827 2719
www.granada-learning.com

Textease 2000 Softease Ltd, Market Place,
Ashbourne, Derbyshire DE6 1ES, Tel 01335 343
421, Fax 01335 343 422
www.softease.com

Talking Write Away Granada Learning/
BlackCat Software, Granada Television, Quay
Street, Manchester M60 9EA, Tel 0161 827 2927
www.granada-learning.com

Dazzle, Fresco Granada Learning, Granada
Television, Quay Street, Manchester M60 9EA,
Tel 0161 827 2927
www.granada-learning.com

Pick a Picture, **Granada Colours** Granada
Learning, Granada Television, Quay Street,
Manchester M60 9EA, Tel 0161 827 2927
www.granada-learning.com

Valiant Roamer, Valiant Technology
www.valiant-technology.com/ideas1.htm

Clicker 4 Crick Software Ltd, Crick House,
Boarden close, Moulton Park, Northampton NN3
6LF, Tel 01604 671691
www.cricksoft.com